BLACK AND WHITE— WRONG AND RIGHT

A True Love Story from South Central

Black and White—
Wrong and Right

A True Love Story
from South Central

Chris Cryer

LUMINARE PRESS
WWW.LUMINAREPRESS.COM

Printed in the United States of America

Luminare Press
442 Charnelton St.
Eugene, OR 97401
www.luminarepress.com

LCCN: 2021916508
ISBN: 978-1-64388-758-6

To Candy, who never saw a dream that could not be fulfilled: Thank you, angel, for showing us the courage, brain, and heart to take on Oz and find our way back home again.

Contents

Author's Note

Black and White/Wrong and Right is a dramatic true story of Candy 17 and Gabe 27, a couple in South Central LA involved in relations legally viewed as statutory rape, illegal in terms of age, but also off limits as teacher and student and unacceptable for many because of racial difference. It even presses the "insult" of matching a Jew with a Christian and a sweet-hearted Mr. Rogers type with a hard-nosed Serena Williams. There is something in this love story to grab almost anyone.

It encompasses the late 1970's through a lifelong marriage, ending in Candy's death in 2014, tracing the suspicion, discrimination, legal threats, and violence she and Gabe suffer, ending in their rise to activism and fame in support of others with relationship rights issues. Exact archival material is presented in this team writing effort, which combines Candy and Gabe's original film script, composed by them as autobiography, with update and conclusion by Will Machin, finally adapted by Chris Cryer into the book form presented here.

Special appreciation belongs to Gabriel Grosz for coordinating and launching the project to share his and Candy's experience in the hope of opening doors for the many who, though culturally or legally mismatched, persist in deep, productive, and enduring relationships. Many portrayed here from the 70's are still friends of Gabe today, forty years later, and the rejuvenation of his story is largely a response to requests he received from nearly everyone he has shared this story with. We who work with him on rebirthing Candy after her death in 2014 become a part of the family, a part of the story. He is a man for all seasons, who clearly has never and will never live a moment of regret.

You Still Have Me

After you look up toward the sky
Locate a star, make a wish
and close your eyes.
Open them and you will see
After all is said and done
You still have me.

Lyrics adapted from "You Still Have Me"
by Singer-Songwriter Candy Billee Mills 1998

CHAPTER ONE

Candy and Gabe in
the Underbelly

South Central, LA in the fall of 1979 was set against a backdrop of the Union Bank Building and ARCO Towers, iconic black shadows sleeping behind a layer of smog that hung over downtown. There were gutters overflowing with trash, spray paint tagged signs, and bar-choked windows next to store fronts with steel grates and mega-locks.

On a corner near Jefferson High, opening early for the first day of classes, a pack of Black guys chug on Colt 45 in paper sacks. One spots something and his eyes narrow. He taps his bruthas with "Yo, check this shit." They look around and spot Gabe Grosz, French, Jewish immigrant and new Health Class teacher on his way to teach his first high school class. He's rhythmically running toward them at a comfortable gait in track shorts and a tank top. At 27, Gabe's stride is phenomenal and his Westside look is cool. His pace is steady, his breathing heavy but controlled. Sweat is streaming down his face. He's been running awhile.

The bruthas stare in amazement as he runs past. Who the fuck is this cracker? Gabe turns down Central Avenue and into the Jefferson campus, overlooking the menacing scene. He focusses on the school, home of his first job, due to start in—he checks his watch—twenty-five minutes. He sees only the edifice of Jefferson, the classrooms, the gym, and God, yes—the track. As a runner, it's his dream job. *By next year we'll have girls' track here*, he muses. *Cross my heart and hope to die.*

Predominantly African American and just south of downtown, Jefferson is as proud as any place in South Central. That's not much, although enough to make students take a smug drag out back, sitting on the concrete where it overlooks the only patch of grass, the athletic field— enough to make them laugh with friends, and talk crap.

In the front, teachers sometimes sit in chats in the thick grass that beautifully sets forth probably the ghetto's best-looking building. Maybe the brothas have extra angst at Jefferson, but nobody is spoiled or pressured by their parents. Most of the teachers know their students' names and "what's up'm" on the way to the locker room, where teachers hang out themselves, never too many at a time.

Everybody is loitering at Jefferson more than working, and isn't that what life's for? No, maybe not for Candy Mills, but she's the "new kid on the block," and she talks "mighty Whitey," "let'n you know when you's wrong" and not wrong often enough herself. She would've been called ass-kicker if she weren't the best runner Jefferson has ever or will ever see. She runs like a Black gazelle, but she talks like a foreigner with a New York spoon in her mouth.

Right up at the school's crab grassy and oddly elegant entrance, a pair of typical thin streets halt, as if finally reaching the only destination without graffiti, pot-holes, stray needles, dilapidation, and general blahs. The students who aren't lurking in front of storefront churches and liquor stores smoking and heckling are often Jefferson's heroes—athletes like Candy, generally on the track running, goofing off, strolling, and spitting out what's more fun in cool company.

Many who found sanctuary at Jefferson in 1979 are still friends today across the far-stretching megalopolis of LA, which has officially buried its infamous neighborhood title for South Central, to hide its violent history forever under the newly worded South LA (SOLA). This is how city administrators try to give the decadent a boost. Jeffersonians can now say, "I'm not from South Central. There ain't no South Central." Many Jeffersonians now proudly use skills they learned from their soon-to-be controversial coach, Gabe Grosz.

But Candy Mills and Gabe Grosz were there long before SOLA, the cool coach pulling in dandelions from the thick front yard and brainy sophomore Candy threading through the back campus, lack-luster crowd, musclemen athletes lounging and spitting in rows all along the muddy front of the athlete locker rooms. They were her friends, her nemeses, her peers, and her teammates. She talked to them straight, no matter what was on her mind. Gabe talked to everybody warmly, teacher lingo spiced with jokes, not in-jokes but friendly ones.

Candy

Candy runs into school every morning and back home later. Does she just run all the time or is she avoiding shit-talk, something she flings as well as anybody when called for? On Gabe's first day at Jefferson, she skirts the art deco false front of the school that has a couple of flowers planted and curved masonry with ridges on the top, slapping cracked concrete all the way to the only (slightly stinky) team showers.

For Candy, new to South Central and feeling trapped there, Black glory, the sweetness, the kind jazz men sing about, seems far away, only played out on the back streets of the French Quarter and in the sophisticated nightclubs of Harlem. Candy's first fourteen years raised as one of few Blacks in Schenectady, New York in the 60's offered no more than flat White, middle class life with nothing particular or even proudly White about it. Now her struggling parents have kidnapped the whole family to infamous South Central, cruelly too Black for its own good.

She slugs out her thoughts in the foot slams of her daily jog to school. Moving with her family from plain White folk to the intensely African American 'hood seems too much, too sudden, too unrewarding. *What about my motivation and my stamina?* Her feet smack out inner, belligerent thoughts. She lunges forward physically but not emotionally. South Central seems like the kind of place to stress you out of your scholarship chances and pull down your track record.

She complains silently to herself, as she performs her daily run, foot-slam by foot-slam, into the campus. At sixteen she should be bored, but never is, just frustrated. Romance can come later, could come later, with the passion to stir things up inside. The romance could come from a man, a place, and a time that fits, that goes somewhere, that means something, something you can sing, something like the Blues warming into Soul. She hums, intentionally and exquisitely on into the lockers, and after considering banging a tin door just for the music of it, throws her sweats into a pile and lavishes upon herself a long, sweet, and quiet shower.

Gabe

Gabe sorts out his first-day class plan in his mind as he veers his pre-class run through the mean streets into sight of Jefferson. He knows when to hurdle over trash, look blankly at pot smokers, and move into a thirty-second lead against his own daily best. At 27 he lives on being reliable and consistent to himself. If this is boring or even limiting, he doesn't know it.

And he doesn't know Candy yet. He doesn't know she approaches school from the south exactly as he approaches from the north nor her similar schedule of running before school, after school on running teams, and for fun. She also runs in hopes of college scholarships, while Gabe has already pocketed his degree and teaching credential. She runs like a 17-year-old girl, gushing with energy and little need to think about control. He runs mature, relaxed, and accomplished. Interestingly, she runs faster and more, but he's a regular and predictable adult, while she's a developing star.

Gabe thinks out his run in punctuated form, as a personal inner rap: *Running's a slug-fest: slug-one, slug-two, slug-three, whoa! Slug-on, slug-on, slug-on, uh! DON'T DRINK, DON'T DATE, DON'T PROCRASTINATE!* He's got a good mantra but only ten minutes til class, and these kids are going to need a perky opener to settle down. *There oughta be a joke. "Runners ain't funners" or something. If I don't keep this class laughing, I know they're gonna eat chalk in Health Class an' track'll turn into spit-ball practice.*

God! There's Smith at the finish, that linear-brained coach who doesn't think Blacks and Whites, Jews and Christians, students and teachers should be seen running the same streets.

Gabe speeds through the open chain link school gate and onto the 440-yard dirt track to complete his run. The imposing Smith, varsity football coach, 40's, Black, muscular, and pleasantly commanding, steps up to comment.

"Yo, Gabe. Over here."

Gabe goes up to him, passing the north goal posts and rounding the far turn to the start/finish line. He takes a glance at his wristwatch and smiles, pleased, while Smith waves a hand in the air. Smith juts out his regular friendly diatribe.

"Morning, coach. What's wrong with you, man? You at it again?"

"At what again?"

"You know what I'm talking about."

"I always take a run before work."

"Maybe in Beverly Hills, but down here in the hood—a White man running—you're liable to get yourself shot."

"It's never been a problem before. I don't think anyone even notices."

Smith eyes him, throwing out, "Get real," and turns and walks away, shaking his head. "You're one crazy dude."

Gabe interrupts, "He who hesitates is . . "

"Dead—" Smith spits out.

"No, man. I'm more like late," says Gabe on his first day to his first class, via a one-minute shower in the gym.

Smith follows him with, "I know you're a late bloomer. Anyway, I've got a babe for you, a good one, a nice girl to go have a drink with—from Brentwood. I know people in Brentwood, too."

"Thanks, but no thanks. I'd rather run than drink." Gabe's only barely preachy, though a one hundred percent role model teacher from over the hill, where Westwood meets the beautiful Brentwood and Brentwood meets the iconic boulevards of Beverly Hills.

"Who said you have to drink?" bleats Smith. "Not all women are in bars. Drink in her eyes!"

"Oh sure. I think I'll just sup up my Health Class!"

Gabe shrugs Smith off with a smile and grabs a towel off the bench, wipes his face, and heads into and quickly back out of the staff locker room.

As Gabe exits MEN, Candy Mills, his student-about-to-be, exits GIRLS. She's an extraordinary Black girl, frankly protégé material.

"Hey, are you Mr. Grosz, the running coach?"

"I'm slated for running coach next year, but in about a minute I'll turn into Mr. Grosz, Health teacher. It's my first day at Jefferson!"

"I heard about you," she squeaks, lightening up. "You're our new teacher from Westwood, from that Jewish high school. You're a-s-t-u-t-e. I know the word, not like 'ass-toot' around here."

"Thanks. I am new. . ." Gabe smirks slyly. "So help me spread the word—'It's gross to call me Grosz!'" He laughs slightly, greeting his first high school student for the first time.

"Oh, I'm on your side, Suh. This place is nothing like Schenectady where I was raised." She turns her head back further down the path and adds, "but the running team and the hurdles at Jefferson could be sweet. . . for me and you next year." Her long-distance squint wrinkles her nose in a cute look that's sweet itself.

"Let's hope so, little lady. Will I see you in class?"

"Yes, Sir. I'm working for a scholarship and . . ." she looks at her watch . . . "we're both half a minute from being late."

Gabe escapes further small-talk and squishes past Candy and through the faculty entrance for classrooms, making it from Gym Hall to class in thirty clocked seconds. Knowing when to run, when to kill time, and when to be on time is pretty much what Jefferson is all about. Guys hanging around in gobs in the dirt yard look like truants who always skip class and never really go home either. Gabe carries his vegan bag lunch with him and a couple of pre-prepped retorts for smartasses in class.

Once inside his classroom, he can hear Candy's beautifully measured footfalls outside the window and is forced to turn around and watch her from there, exquisitely sprinting to his class.

"I bet you run Brentwood on weekends," she streams across the sidewalk and into his face at the window.

"I do!" he shouts back.

At this point the class fills with jumbled bodies, seemingly unwilling to sit down and face front. Candy finally emerges among them, the only one carrying an armload of books. Gabe writes in chalk across the top of the blackboard "Health Education." Once seats are more or less filled, he turns his back to his first class ever and spells his name out assertively: "MR. GROSZ," all caps, in large block letters, striking each letter in determination . . . G-R-O-S-Z!

He turns and confronts thirty students, mostly Blacks and a few Latinos. They buzz and bullshit inattentively, but Gabe presses on:

"And it's *Mister* Grosz,"

Candy Mills is seated near the back. She's neatly dressed, pretty, with short hair and an athletic body. She's the only one paying attention. While Gabe organizes and glares down his group, she primes her materials and prepares to take notes, something that appears to be a foreign skill at Jefferson.

Gabe continues his introduction. "It's NOT Cuz, Blood, Ese, Homey, Cholo, or Buddy." A snicker goes through the class, not a buddy kind of crowd, when a Black student in the back of the room blurts out, "What about Whitey?" and Gabe takes the hit of an unleashed class overcome with laughter. But he chokes this one down and answers in perfect rebound, "LOOK, young man. Show a little respect. That's Mr. Whitey to you." The kids crack up again, but this one is his win. He settles in, breathes better, and privately delights in the moan and mime rhapsody of his new, very own and already slightly beloved, Jefferson High.

Candy, 1980, the Second Year at Jefferson

Munching on popcorn and Kool-Aid on a porch glider with her mom, Candy gets cranky in the September South Central heat, famous for its choking blend of over-ripe citrus, smog, and car exhaust. She moans at her mom.

"Since we're not exactly in Whiteville anymore, I guess we're in Bluesville Ghetto," she complains. "You sold our soul for LA glitz. This is not the Black Shangri-la you and dad expected." She slowly sighs, then yawns. "We had Ralph Bunch at Jefferson, but when was that?"

"Honey, that was in the 20's, when all South Central was white-bread. I remember when he talked about our little neighborhood in the 50's, when he won the Nobel Peace Prize. He didn't forget this place. But your aunt sure did. She just led us on out here from New York on a whim an' practically disappeared. I jus' call'r Diana Ross. She's out there float'n in society somewhere.

I hope she goes to Florida like she said she'd do, 'cause it takes guts 'n devotion to live in this pollution park. But we can do it, Baby. We can do it cause we're all smart in this family, and you run'n every day, your A grades, an' all your sports! At least we have two Black churches here, Sweetie. You need the grace of a Black God with ya more'n you were ever gonna see it in Schenectady. These churches is ladies and gentlemen from our own culture.

I wanted this for you, Candy, and you can walk to school. It's a good school. And you're run'n track and win'n! If we could just poke through the air o' this place, I believe we'd see the far-off Hollywood Sign up there, right over there off this porch, just a little bit. I bet we could."

Candy hugs DeLois, her pretty, white-shoed, white-dressed nurse-mom, totally devoted to progress and culture for her dilapidated but striving family. She is the kind of mom who talks deeply to one or another of her kids the whole time she does her laundry or washes her dishes. She stops now to remove her white shoes, wipe them off with a damp cloth and line them up in front of the glider. She's tired as usual and sighs right into Candy's face.

"Don't worry, Mommy. You brought me up to bring up the rest of us, and I am. I'm doing it, but you'll never see the Hollywood Sign from here. I'll tell you what, though. Mr. Gabe is taking some of us this weekend. We're starting runs to the top of the Hollywood Sign on Saturdays. It's just voluntary, but we'll carpool to Los Feliz and run around and over Griffith Park, about five miles to the sign. Once

I've got the hang of it, I'll take you too. Wasn't Dorothy Dandridge at Jefferson too?"

Candy's very proper mom steps back in a serious glare.

"Excuse me, Miss Mills, my dear little (okay, not so little) tom-boy, did you say 'Mr. Gabe?' We don't call teachers by their first names in this household. I didn't scrape to send all four of you to private schools in, as you call it, Whiteville, for nothing. You know better. As for Dorothy Dandridge, she was long before my time, but she was from here. In fact, a lot o' the 30's jazzmen were from Jefferson. They were at the Dunbar Jazz Club. You could o' walked there from here. Jeff'son was the first big Black high school in LA. S'pose that's why my sista led us out here. She probably thinks we're the Herb Jeffries. . . He was the Black cowboy who went west too.... Pioneers o' the Black race, wandr'n painfully outa White Schenectady for fame in the LA melt'n pot!"

"Well, wait 'n see our new fame in sport," Candy laughs. "I'm on it, and I'm onto Mr. Gabe, too." She winks with no explanation and starts to leave the porch.

"Wait a minute, little Daddy's boy. Don't let your father get to ya. You're no boy, and you just act like a lady whatever you do or say. You may make two of your brother and dream of awards, and music, and sports stars, and even win yourself, but you're a lady first. If you start spending all your time with that track team, you just call a spade a spade, and that would not be 'Mr. Gabe.' You just call him 'Suh.'"

Candy returns to hug her mom.

"Yes, ma'am, Mommy. I'll try to think of Mr. Gabe as 'Suh,' and as for dreaming Watts-style dreams, I think after I finish the Olympics and college, I'll sing jazz, just like the South Central singers used to. Mommy, I love you. You had a long day. Just sit here and have some more Kool-Aid. I'm pretty peppy. Don't worry. I'm sure I'll do it all."

Gabe 1980

Mundane challenges are enough for Gabe. He has no secrets, no fantasies, no need to date. Contrary to what Candy's mother suggests, and a few others, he is not gay. Just content. Why aren't more people concerned with living the food pyramid, packing their vegan lunches and outrunning their personal bests? The teaching that goes with coaching is a thorn in his side, but he's getting the hang of it and probably teaches as many corny jokes as points of health.

Coaching is becoming everything to him, and he enjoys it calmly, the way connoisseurs savor the aroma of wine, swishing it around their glasses. He tempers competition until it has no aggression. There is no need to box your way through a running track, only to commune with it and your energy.

Candy likes to work with him. He never belittles anybody on the team, and like her, never has enough of it. He's always the last to leave and the first with new places to run, new times, and trials. Once the Hollywood Sign runs get started, though, they are not weekly, but often. The ten miles round trip from Griffith Park to the sign and back are still not enough for Candy. She asks for more, and it's hard to turn her down. She almost has a right to her obsession. You couldn't warn her about needing more study time, her physical condition, or wasting time. She'd already aced everything, got along with her parents, made top grades, received track awards and stats continuing to move up, and was even better at sprinting and, for God's sake, hurdles.

"Maybe you need to settle into some more fun, guys and stuff," Gabe suggests. "Take a break and relax."

After that, she simply balks and says, "Gee, I'd rather go for Olympic training down the line."

At this thought, Gabe's neck-length, Jesus-style hair feels like it's curling from the inside out.

"God! You should," he says. "But I'm not going to be Simon Legree. We need to talk. This may be more exciting to me than it is to you."

In a way, Gabe and Candy were the same. They came from and lived in different universes but not when it came to the part of life they cared about. That was the same. He'd always loved running as the basis of his balanced life; she desperately needed running to balance her confusion over destiny askew. At 28, he had a lifetime of successful years beyond her, but for 16, her ability to pluck skills was phenomenal. Adolescents and adults don't value things in the same way, but Candy and Gabe had steel-tempered passion for the same thing.

How pretty was she, how sexy? And Gabe of the beautiful Jesus look, long-haired, tan, with a runner's body and sincere eyes? They didn't know how they looked or care. No one mentioned or thought about that. It was school and running that threw them together, Gabe charismatic, with his fun, cool image and Candy exquisitely disciplined, toned, and too smart not to talk truth. They were an arresting pair of individuals. Together on a run or at a race, they fit each other like pieces in a puzzle no one perceived but themselves.

They were like quick-minded Serena Williams and soft-hearted Mr. Rogers. They shared more than runners' mania. They shared long-winded dreams that held back their spirit toward a 60's-style better world: more exercise, power food, wrenching songs, open relationships, and freer love. Individually, Candy enjoyed the clear-sighted confidence of a female Malcolm X, while Gabe's attitude and body were as lean and tuned as an exploring Jacques Cousteau. Candy loved history and she wanted to make history. Gabe wanted to escort her through the ghetto to that better place.

This combination made music. They didn't know what kind it would be. They didn't sense that, like John Lennon, they might run into walls against imagination—against "living for today." They didn't consider that, like the gyrations of Elvis, originally seen as demoralizing, any movement between them might stop clocks and run a red light in the Halls of Justice.

Gabe and Candy's Second Year at Jefferson

Next year, they'll face hell's test of love together, but at 29 Gabe is reshaping a sea of third-rate expectation, comfortable as a token nonconformist and campus icon. Candy finds seventeen her coming-out party. She is increasingly a winner for her team, her school, and her family, and she continues to peak despite the ups and downs everybody experiences in the shadow of the Crips and Bloods.

The two super-runners begin to get comfortable in the underbelly. Candy begins stopping by Gabe's open-class brown bag lunch times with other track team kids. The peer language is rough even for her, but there's a runner mentality that holds them together in a kind of athletes' pride. Runners are not exactly the gamey figures in sports.

As they start approaching just before noon one day, Candy arrives first to find the last class in overtime and waits in the hall by the open door. There's standard banter inside.

Gabe asks, "Anyone care to read the title this homework's about?"

Sheila, a female student, blurts out, "I never learned to read, Mr. Grosz," while the group shifts out of the classroom and towards the hall like a released herd, murmuring and cooing. "Yeah," answers a perky male student, turning back from the doorway. "We was all absent that week."

"Read it at home, then," Gabe urges the hoard, and Candy enters just before her track-peers. She hands Gabe a clipping from the *Schenectady Gazette*.

"What's this?" He adjusts his reading glasses into full teacher mode, and she says nothing, as he unfolds the clipping and reads the small headline. "Candy's Dandy as a Girl Sprinter Can Be."

"I want you to know how much I love to compete," she announces, watching his eyes for approval.

Gabe changes gear, acting suddenly like a paid recruiter. "Wow! One of the fastest in all of New York last year, and still a freshman. I'm, uh, I'm impressed."

Candy becomes self-conscious. He studies her and her sudden show of shyness, and at that moment, there is almost a hint of something between them, a connection. But it's shattered like a whirlwind, when members Anthony and Erwin of the track team burst in through the front door, and two more, Neal and Tyrus through the rear. The four boys converge on Gabe and Candy at Gabe's desk, and Candy inches close to Gabe, clutching her books like a shield.

Buddy Neal breaks into rap—

"Hey Grosz!
What's up home'boy?

15

> Dad-dy Neal is here for real
> All the girls want a piece o' me
> Chunk o' my mas-cu-lin-i-ty
> I'm tall. I'm dark and I'm
> You know it—handsome
> Stronger than King Kong and—"

Tyrus cries, "Nigga, you look more like Nilla Gorilla." Anthony and Erwin burst into laughter.

"Fuck—ya'll!" Neal retaliates, until Gabe halts the scene.

Gabe breaks in, "Hey, cool it with the language, you primal mates!"

This sends Neal strutting to the window to preen in the sun and unleashes Tyrus to investigate Candy's clipping and *Runner's World* from the desk. They're Candy's materials, and Gabe lunges automatically, more like a sensitive Ninja than a running coach, reclaims them and returns them to her in one swift move.

"Okay, okay, man!" Tyrus backs off. "So, we runnin' today, Grosz?"

"*Mister* Grosz and yes, Tyrus," Gabe announces, picking up an eraser to clean off the board to settle down with his brown-bag vegan sandwich.

Anthony, catching a piece of chalk tossed by Erwin, pipes in, "Not yet, coach, I'm mak'n you a Popeye cartoon to watch ya eat yer spinach."

Gabe checks out and erases Popeye with a fatherly grimace, while Tyrus says, "I'm in. Cool. Keepin' in shape 'case the po-lice chase. Hey, I made a rhyme."

Neal struts over to Candy and checks her up and down, causing Gabe to put down his food. "What's up, Mama?" Neal asks her.

But before she answers, Gabe commandeers his lunch scene, standing up with an ultimatum. "Guys, either behave yourselves or get out!"

Candy acknowledges the hood moment with an idle smile, as Anthony grabs the chalk from Erwin and starts to draw Popeye again. The "men" draw closer to the door and deeper into insult.

Neal snickers at   Anthony, "Yeah, boy, he ain't play'n."

"Shut the fuck up, Nigga," Anthony finishes.

"Hell, Grosz," Erwin tries to close. "That's what's wrong with young bruthas today. No respect!"

A blast of hood-talk ensues that ties up lunchtime pretty much the same way everything else gets tied up at Jefferson. For Candy and Gabe, it was not the day it started out to be. They both sat down and ate their sandwiches silently to the rap theater of four guys neither would invite to Sunday dinner but both treasured on the track. They were wondering the same thing, why they so-loved these guys that made life like living in a family full of bad-ass little kids, who neither eat nor sleep, just continually get and stay in your way.

Neal: "Yo Mama, Erwin."

Erwin: "Why you gotta bring my Mama into this, man?"

Neal: "I'll talk about yo Mama and yo ugly-ass sista and all the other apes in yo family, Nigga."

Erwin: "Talk about my family again and I'll stomp yo pretty boy ass!"

Gabe moves closer to Candy to lighten her scene and peek at her lunch. He says, "Hard to believe these guys are best of friends. Crazy, huh?"

"Low brow," she murmurs under her breath. "It's just ape-shit."

At this, Neal flies back with "Yeah, crazy like you, Grosz, except I'm tall, dark, and handsome, and you're not. Yee hee!" He snatches the *Runners' World* from Tyrus, who snatches it back, ripping it and leaving Neal with a handful of tattered pages.

Tyrus takes a stand with Grosz. "Look it what Neal done!"

"That's . . . that was part of my collection," Gabe whines back. "Would you stop acting like clowns?" He begins to arrest this group in a half-buddy-half spent-teacher stare.

Neal, however, stays feisty, with no sense of Candy's possessions or what conversation she and Grosz had begun about her future career. He says, "Come on, Grosz. You know if this fine little Mama wasn't up there, you'd be workin' things just like us Niggas."

Anthony covers for Gabe with, "We ain"t no Niggas, Nigga. You the most Nigga I ever seen, Neal."

At this digression, Tyrus grabs part of the torn-out pages from him, offers them to Gabe and says, "I didn't mess with your magazine, Grosz. You saw it was Mandingo done the rippin'."

"Bitch!" Neal yells. "Watch who you call'n Mandingo! I'll beat the Black ass offa y'all."

Grosz rebounds. "All right, people. That's enough!"

Which Erwin mimics: "Yeah, gosh darn it, people."

The boys look at each other and laugh uproariously, while Neal struts back to the window to preen some more. He says, "Aw, don't sweat it. Grosz. I'll get ya'll another magazine, homeboy."

This unleashes Tyrus, who slowly moans out, "He can't get you one, Grosz. He ain't got no mo-ney!"

Neal quickly walks back and gets in his face, murmuring, "Ain't nobody said nothing about buying shit."

Finally Anthony ends it all with "Kick'm out, Grosz!"

Once Gabe advances to settle the melee, arms outstretched, he begs, "Gentlemen," in calming tones and with a let's-settle-the whole thing disposition. "I'm asking you for the last time to watch your language. There's a lady present."

"What lady?" burps Tyrus into his Coke, causing the rest to scoff in obnoxious howls.

Candy stands embarrassed, as luckily the boast-hardy shift on out. Neal offers a thumbs-up to Gabe, leaving with, "This shit's straight-up lame. Later, Grosz." Anthony and Tyrus shift on out too.

Erwin turns to Candy sweetly. "Don't mind them. They can't help it. My name's Erwin. What's yours?"

But Candy just looks at Gabe shyly.

"Why you have to look at Mr. Grosz? You don't know your own name?"

She answers this saying, "My name's Candy."

Erwin's not satisfied. He's nosey and rants, "Why you talk like that?"

She just turns to Gabe again, confused, until she builds resolve and steamily throws out a, "Like what?"

Then the true shit she's really tired of comes out. He says, "Like you're White."

This time she unleashes the steely gaze and slowed, perfect elocution of a lawyer in court. "That's just the way I talk." About to ask him if he doesn't have another class to go to, she begins to scoop up the remnants of her torn press release.

He drones on about what city she's from.

Eyes cast on the floor, she answers "Schenectady.... upstate New York."

"Oh, you mean Connecticut." Erwin starts to feel more connected.

Candy persists in talking down to him. "No. Connecticut's not a city."

At this point, poor Erwin is losing the argument and lashes out, "Hey, I knew that. What do you think I am, undereducated?"

Erwin adds, "How you spell 'Schenectady'?"

Despite all three being on their knees collecting the last scraps of Candy's article, she spells aloud the long indigenous word, to his shock.

"Damn! I get it. A lot of White people live there, right?"

"Yeah," she answers.

They're all on their feet again with his in-her-face proclamation.

"See. That's why you talk like that."

Then three sets of eyes confirm their togetherness, til Candy looks again at Gabe, which Erwin jumps on like a psychiatrist unlocking the phobia of a lifetime.

"Why you keep looking at Mr. Grosz? Every time I say something, you look at Mr. Grosz. What's up with that, girl?"

Gabe's now really punch drunk himself, lowering a stiff "Leave her alone, Erwin!" Which Erwin prefers to see as a tone-mellowing opportunity to side back up to Candy the way he meant to in the first place.

"Mama, am I bothering you?"

Candy's eyes ride back to Gabe questioningly, til she breaks into giggles. The other guys choke and act uncomfortable.

"Your whole face lights up when you smile," Erwin croons more than ever, til she starts to pick up her books, using them to hide her smile.

"Don't ever hide that face," he continues, sticking his ugly nose near hers behind her book façade. "Why you wanna hide your face? It's nice. She's got a pretty smile, huh, Grosz?"

"You're embarrassing her," Gabe warns.

"Well, doesn't she?" comes the rebound.

"SHE DOES HAVE A NICE SMILE!" Gabe admits. "SHE DOES! So, enough for today. Everybody get outa here! Erwin, shut up and give all the mothers and me a rest."

In an act similar to the burst of energy that dropped this crowd into Gabe's lap 40 minutes ago, the guys instantly burst out again, their raucous tenor escalating in echoes down the hall.

Gabe concludes another extra-curricular lunch event, this time gathering up the sweet remaining silence to bow in a teacherly way to Candy. "You are a lady, quite a lady, Candy. If you want to bring your Schenectady reputation with you, we sure need it. Don't let any of these guys get in your way."

It was just another day at Jefferson High. All insults aside, few high grades are brewing, but the camaraderie is. Despite the tone of things, the runners hold tight, and Candy's role on the team blooms in extraordinary ways on and off the track.

Candy

Rethreading her laces with Juana in Griffith Park, Candy sits in a grass patch by a dirt path, facing the Hollywood Sign, still miles away.

"I can smell it," she says.

"Oh yeah. You can smell anything," Juana pipes in. "I'm smell'n a win Saturday 'cause you can smell SUC'-cess! Man, Grosz's running us in circles and nobody else's out here practicing on weekends, gett'n outa their shit-hole school. I'd be for do'in all the practice out here if we had the time. I'm tired, but this air is like fuel. If I don't make it all the way, I know you will, 'n that means I'll get the baton anyway. I'm get'n a lot outta runn'n weekends, 'win'r-lose' this gold standard of Grosz's."

Candy exhales slowly, as though it's a comment. "I know what you mean. My mama wants to come out here with us, but it's hard enough getting her to the meet. I can hardly get my studying done at home. If the sun weren't sinking when we get there, I'd love to jus' study right there, underneath the sign. But, of course, we'll be exhausted. It's funny that you just don't feel it once you're out of school. Oh, my God, here comes Grosz. He's going to pair off running with somebody who'll listen to his hero-runner stories."

"That's so funny," Juana giggles. How can he run, coach, 'n tell dramatic winner stories at the same time? It does'n work for me. I jus crack up and can't run. He's gonna pair off with you though. You too tolerant, Baby."

"That's just because it hypnotizes me and I turn into a running zombie. I could run forever when he's right there chanting, 'Run, hun, jus like Ry'un!'"

"Suzy-Q, watch out. You gonna fall in love, and when you wake up, you won't find a prince. You gonna find a WHITE MAN stand'n there."

The two scream and giggle at that thought, ending in a long crazy laugh.

"I could do worse for a running peer," Candy beams. "If I went into a hypnotic runner's trance and woke up with a trophy in my hand, I'd take the guy, even if I was blind-folded. As for putting up with vegan box lunches, hero stories and stupid chants and cheers—really boring ones, 24/7 drudgery, and the meekest-meanest coach in the world—We really LUCKY! Just don't tell nobody!"

Candy is strong, strong-willed and strong-hearted. She can and does speak Schenectian and South Centralese at will, as needed. But she doesn't need much. She has it made, and she begins to know it, as smart women do. They know when their magic is moving into a sphere and sense where it leads. She knows she can run, hurdle, and ace classes. She knows she has a future in both camps, and she knows that Gabe is a piece of good luck, a kind of missing link to pull her universe together that will probably never come together for her mom, her family, and especially her dad. He's been acting strange at home, lately, and—well, getting out of the house right now is a blessing.

Gabe

Gabe is only a little bit full of himself, only in the right ways. His role at Jefferson is building up fast. He's Mr. Fortitude, chucking his sliver of a White body every day all along the parameters of the campus and the railroad tracks and dragging his team with him across LA to his chosen goal post—the Hollywood Sign. A lot of people try to stop him along the way, winos with inane questions, little old ladies wanting to talk about the weather, and an occasional pumped-up Crip egging him for a stand-off.

One morning on the edge of campus, it's so dark he can hardly see who's there, when a shower of pebbles comes at him from the front and one side. He loves to run along the railroad tracks there but has never seen, in a better light, any pebbly spots. He knows the terrain like the back of his hand and immediately shakes with fear of the obvious, someone playing games. You don't play games where the

Crips and Bloods hang out. Everything off is pure street gang, and he knows to hold the adrenaline and tense every cell, also to stay calm as hell. He decides to try to look even calmer and slows down very casually, as if planning to take it easy on a slope from the rails and have a break.

He wants to jerk his head karate style at the source but doesn't even look in that direction. He stops and crouches, acting like someone ready to pull out a cigarette. Then his teacher skills take over, and he looks up to see a dark figure, pelting him, the outline of a teen-ager trying to stone him to death. He wants to lunge at him but realizes the dark might hide a knife, so he flattens out his shock to an amazingly calm, "Hey, Man, what're you doing? Stop throwing stones. What's the point?" He tries to say this like a disappointed friend, but—"HERE'S the point!" is the answer—a gun in a shrouded right hand shoved at him at a distance of very few feet.

The fact that no one else is there to help rings through Gabe's head like a shock wave, as does the thought that no one can hear him yell for help. All Gabe has at this moment is his incredible, inexhaustible earnestness, and he decides to play it like Jesus talking to Pontius Pilate.

"Listen," he bids. "Let's just let it go, okay? Let's cool it? Why not?"

He stands up, turns slowly and carefully, and pulls away into a sudden run with the gait of a bullet. He makes it back to campus, safety, and a warm spreading sunrise that stops totally. The moment and the win are profoundly serene.

With days like this, Gabe knows he has become a part of the new Wild West, laced with sundown and sun-up showdowns, putting notches in his belt, and being sure everybody knows he is a man. Oddly, it leaves him thinking of Candy who runs the same hours and neighborhood every day. At this moment, he decides firmly to tell her she should not run alone anymore, and so they start right away to run together.

Somehow Candy and Gabe also have in common that they are both stable personalities cursed every day with having to shirk the hood. How Candy and Gabe found themselves in the birth home of the Crips and Bloods is a wonder, the same wonder we all have about the intersection of history and fate. They find themselves there literally, and it speaks to them.

Candy's family followed the diaspora of Blacks who genuinely sought certain spots in the US targeting advancement for Blacks. Her aunt, who instigated the move from Schenectady to LA, was off in her timing, though, as the LA Black Renaissance, which was real in the 40's long predated her urge for the move. The history, *The Great Black Way* by R.J. Smith, outlines "a wave of Black migration to a small area of LA along Central Avenue" in the heart of South Central, a startling group of significant cultural development. The community was due in part to FDR opening the defense industry to Blacks at the same time the US began to see the earliest start toward civil rights thinking.

Gabe fell into all this with much less pre-meditation than Candy's family. After living with his sister and widowed mom south of the famous Sunset Strip and just west of downtown, he moved into an apartment alone in nearby Westwood, close to UCLA. When the phone rang with an offer to teach his first class ever, he fell for the "combat pay" in South Central, several thousand dollars more than for teaching elsewhere. Risk was the farthest thought from his mind, and for him, the money and the challenge loomed way beyond common sense. After one quick phone conversation, he packed up to move and filled his pockets with the top level acumen of his own high school experience, Fairfax High, a mostly-Jewish public school he lived near, rated number one in the city. He headed straight for Jefferson, rated number 49 out of 49 schools and one of the three toughest.

Though stand-up comic for the lock-down crowd, Gabe almost drops out of teaching "cool" in his first days. But when he discovers the students can't really read beyond a lower elementary level, he collects elementary materials and adapts them to deep appreciation so that text theft becomes his greatest new problem. His simplifying of schoolwork and playing out the comic moves him straight through the contest at hand. It's after celebrating this success his runner's passion bites and holds him.

When he discovers there's no girls' track team, he stalks the principal with the idea of creating one. With never a moment of self-questioning, he knows he can do it, and well, and he knows the girls can do it as well, not to mention Candy. Not only does he help develop long-distance runners for the boys' team, but later, running into Candy and other lithe girls, he recruits relentlessly for a girls' team, and quickly brings both teams into the LA Southern League and eventually into championship finals.

South Central and Westwood are one in Gabe, and he runs his teams straight from one neighborhood to the other. His daily 10-mile, 30-minute drive to work from one universe to another is a sprint, a cocktail for him. He never really wanted to teach as much as to coach, and he figures out Jefferson is the place where the coaching is going to happen.

South Central has been a constantly changing neighborhood, and it may have been at its most dangerous during Gabe and Candy's late 70's, when there was little diversity. Eventually, integration of LA waters down some of the racism, reducing levels of violence. It is minimally Black today and a working mixture of Latinos, Asians, and Blacks. More people were out on the streets there in those days than now. Today fear of risk everywhere is endemic, and average American children don't know much about the streets. For Candy and Gabe, running daily in South Central in the late 70's is a singular event. There really is plenty of risk but little sense of it for them. For those two, running goals superseded fear.

American children were raised in those days with one main suggestion from their parents, "Go out and play!" When the sun went down, kids came home, along with their dogs; the lights went on, and the streets most places were quiet. But South Central is special. It's where street gangs begin, and Candy and Gabe are there to see it fester. One of Gabe's students, for instance, is suddenly and criminally gunned down on the corner of San Pedro and 64th Street. He is not a gang member, but walking with Ray Washington, a top Crip leader, and very close to school. Gabe has gang members in his classes, but he and they hold their own code of respect for each other that is never broken despite the violent events of a typical week.

Gabe's plan to get those teens out of lock-down, off their own streets, and over to the green hills of Griffith Park on weekends is more than therapy. He is the first to do it, but one of his runners, later a track coach himself, sees the power of it, and resumes the tradition today.

With her two feet solidly, one in each culture, Candy understands the need to run with Gabe even more than he does to run with her. She asks him to start doing their daily sunset runs together too, and it is the first relationship they have—two runners merging into each night's new darkness, no longer ever alone. The metaphor fits them perfectly.

They start Jefferson's first female track team, he as coach and she quickly as star runner. Together they predictably bloom for their school.

CHAPTER TWO

Pandora's Box

Gabe

It's Gabe's last year as a young adult. At 28 he's rethinking holding back, remaining shy, and his right to personal idiosyncrasies. Candy, 17, now a Black athletic princess, is on the brink in a similar way, about to lose her right to teen-age confusion, backsliding and rants. Fate intermingles with all of this, and the result is success. Jefferson sees the track teams really step up for the gold, and Gabe is predestined to set the goal Candy achieves. Underneath all this, hides something else they share. Despite their new reputations as busy athletes, they're both lonely.

Gabe wakes up one morning at 5:00 am thinking of Candy, dreaming of a conversation he shared with her long before she and the teams were on the upsurge. He remembers her slacking off, full of herself from her days in New York when she was hurdling and sprinting in a state without California-level fame and expectation. She'd been slacking off when they met, and he sometimes deeply regrets yelling at her as her coach, but he needed to set her straight, and they rarely slid back into disappointments between themselves again.

The dream, a replay of a real time together, leaves him sweaty in bed with the depression of what had been repetitive stress and fuss with her. It's like watching a movie he already knows well. He can repeat almost every word between them. He can't forget the things he said because it shocked him then and the shock continues, enough to become a dream. He's bug-eyed watching and hearing himself at his worst:

The Dream

"You know what your problem is?" and the answer pounds and reverberates in the dream. "Too much talent! Not enough heart!"

Candy seems lethargic and sort of swims around the room in cavalier responses. "I'm allergic to the sun, Grosz."

He sits up and stares in a long mental replay of how it'd been. "Is that so?"

An uncaring Candy replies, "Can I go now?"

"No, I have more to say."

"Why are you always getting on my case?

"Getting on your case? That's not my thing. I've got better things to do than to pick on one of my runners."

"I don't see you coming down on anybody else, only me."

"The fact of the matter is—you're the only one on the team that gives me such a hard time. I don't know what you did, what they let you get away with in New York, but you can't waltz in here and do whatever the hell you want. You can't walk off the field in the middle of practice. What kind of example are you setting for the other girls?"

"Why do I have to be an example?"

"Because they look up to you. They know you're the stand-out athlete on the team. And if I let you get away with it, everybody'll slack off."

"It's only a sport, Mr. Grosz. Give me a break."

"It's not just a sport. It's your sport, and you haven't even finished one workout all season. Not one!"

He is reminded in this dream that she tried to slip away from him, around the side toward the door, but he blocked her, physically standing in her way, and his feelings are mixed up with her life, but she is his student? He could've just sent her tardy slips and annotated her records. Heaven forbid, he could've had a conference with her parents.

Still feeling bad about something harsh he'd done way last year, he sits up in bed and goes into double-shock, a sort of shock at his own shock. He knows he's a good coach. He knows things are now going great, but he can't believe he is so unleashed over any student, over what's, as Candy would say, just a job. Something about himself is haunting him, though he's broken no rules, is totally correct in his discipline, and . . . maybe that's it . . . he'd won the argument in the short term and in the long term. It hits him that they are increasingly playing a very large role in each other's lives. He thinks now that he overstepped and that she is radically changed, in her own favor, because of it.

On the surface it's coach and runner, but something else he cannot see any way to change is there, too. Somewhat numb and sweaty, he sits quietly and intentionally runs through the rest of that experience in his memory. It's amazing that he recalls the entire encounter so bitterly and in so much detail. Both her words and his ring out, as if he should never have spoken to her again. But, of course, everything sprang back to normal, to better than normal afterwards. Yet something he cannot get to the bottom of feels deeply wrong and unresolved:

"I'm not done," he continues to spit out in the dream. "You're either part of the team or you're out! That means finishing your workouts so you can finish your races big time. Don't forget— 'Quitters never win and winners never quit.'"

"You tell some jokes at the wrong time, Mr. G., I always win."

"This isn't New York, honey. Lots of girls in this state are fast. I'm talking about girls who run for Dorsey, Manual Arts, Locke."

"I'll win."

"Come back here, young lady."

"I don't have to listen to you!"

"You walk around here with your nose up in the air. Well, it takes a lot more than that to be a champion."

"Why are you so tough on me? Because I don't worship you like everybody else?"

"Because what you have is worth fighting for."

At that, he remembers Candy's eyes shifting away, and Gabe's tone shifts entirely. It becomes soft, almost broken, and he feels tired and defeated as he continues: "You've got so much going for you, Candy. Most of the kids here lead a tough life with plenty to worry about. But, they run their butts off. They give it everything they've got. You, with all the academic and athletic talent you have, can be anything you want. But you're your own worst enemy."

Slowed down then, he let out a heartfelt sigh, and sunk onto a bench, which as the memory ends, turns into his bed. He'd been more defeated than she, which did not seem right, and he looked up into her toned sprinter body standing over him when he finished all he could say on the matter, and he stared at it in its perfection, her eyes in all their complexity and intelligence, and felt her soul. This was more than he felt right to be acquainted with.

"There's a lot more to being a winner, Candy, than finishing in first place."

At this, she'd met him in the dream in that soft place emotional exhaustion takes us, and looked into his face in a neutral way, fiercely held back the stinging comments she is so capable of, and in amazing silence and control, left the locker room. Gabe dreamed he slammed a locker door after she left, though he was not the kind of person to do such a thing. He'd then sat on the bench alone for a minute and gradually remembered he was a coach. He'd finally remembered what else he was supposed to be doing, and surprisingly awakened to what had not really happened.

Post Dream

But today, in a dream, the drama and its feeling come back and somehow bring everything to a stop. The dream demands attention. There is something important in it to deal with. After that, no tardy slips are filed and no parent conferences are held. Instead, as if she had been waiting for a rescuer, she starts to ask his advice, and begins the climb toward sprinter and hurdler champion.

Sitting in bed, as the sunlight crosses the horizon, Gabe wipes his wet chest and arms with the sheet and can start to get comfortable again with the positive reality of incredible track team success since then. But he is struck by the significance of dreaming. In that moment he suddenly senses why he dreamed about that day and more reasons why it is disturbing for him.

It was good to stop her in her tracks. It was good that he reset her goals and the team was on the rise. But there is more to it, and he doesn't understand what. Why is the most complicated person he ever met so at his bidding now? What is he supposed to do with that power? They can run races, train, and win, but there is something funny at the end of it all. For one thing, it doesn't end.

There's more you have to do after the meet, and more before it. There's a lot more. It's good for the sport that they relate the way they did that day. But after his dream therapy, he starts to wonder what's good and what's not, because something else is making him feel not good, and he can't fix what he doesn't understand. What is unleashing inside of Gabe we may know, but Gabe truly does not.

Candy

Candy's nightmare is not subconscious. It's real. She's confused, too, but she knows a lot more than he does. She knows, as the female does, to stand over him at the locker room bench and say nothing. She knows her power as only a shrew knows to say cutting things but also to suddenly say nothing. There's nothing as powerful as refusing an argument to an arguer, especially at the point in the argument when you win. Also, Gabe is the best thing that has ever happened to her life, and she endears him enough to lay aside her sizable debate skills for the first time ever in a peace accord of sorts. She wants to thank him for getting upset with her, but in her exquisite womanly wisdom, she knows this would cross a line, become too personal. She knows they have already crossed several lines that he for his vast professionalism will not mention.

Candy's unslept nightmare is about what to do with her power over him, never realizing he is frozen over the sudden realization that he has so much power over her. She knows, between them, she is in control, and she works not to exert it on his less-knowing nature. All these powers at bay are always and increasingly her nightmare, power over the team, the coach, dating guys, her mother, and sadly over her father's conduct on nights when he wanders the house in the middle of the night. She wants and needs to be even bitchier to get it off her shoulders. She comes to a new decision instead, to let out her tender self by confiding just a little in Gabe at times when she can find a way.

Jefferson on the Map

Candy has other reasons to feel her oats. The previous year's big city meet, the 1980 Los Angeles City Track and Field Championship, has put Jefferson High on the map and into history. It was her move, her victory, that lifted the school rank for relay from last place to second. This affected everything, moving her from dreamer to achiever, from key player to a winner loved by all, not to mention her coach.

A glance back at 1980 shows how nervous the female Jefferson sprinters were. They were the strength of a team that included boys' track, trained somewhat inadvertently by the football coach, and now for the first time, girls' track, trained by Gabe. *The Los Angeles Times* predicted Jefferson would place sixth in the 880-yard medley relay, and Gabe's girls were just happy to have made it to the championship at all.

At the start of the relay the stadium was packed with standing room only. Lane assignments placed Jefferson in their green and gold exactly where the *Times* saw them, in lane six. Sheila was there, baton in hand, next to the runner from Locke, next to, in the outside lane, someone from Westchester. The crowd roared intensely for these female-sprinters. They all took their marks and were set. The starter raised his pistol and fired, and the school-girl racers exploded out of the blocks.

The first 110-yard leg was close, as Sheila passed the baton to Juana, who ran the second 110-yard leg. As she handed off to Dawn, Jefferson fell back to their predicted sad fate, second to last. Next Dawn completed her 220-yard leg, reaching out to Candy for the anchor 440 yards. But at this point, Jefferson fell back to last. Suddenly, bug-eyed, the crowd rose to their feet as they saw Candy fly by one, two, three runners on the first straight-away. The excitement grew to a deafening level as she flew by yet another runner on the final curve, pulling Jefferson from seventh to second. She chased down the first-place runner, nearly catching her at the tape, and finished second!

The final results were: Manual Arts, Fremont, Jefferson, Washington, Crenshaw, Locke, Kennedy, and Westchester. Juana, Dawn, and Sheila mobbed Candy and rejoiced. Candy, of course, took it all in stride.

The significance for Candy is that she sees a lot of envy fade from her team members and begins to feel like a real athlete who might achieve the scholarships she seeks every day of her driven life. She starts to relax more with the other runners, who clearly appreciate her for the first time on every level.

Her 1980 victory has less effect on her closeness with Gabe because they have the same level of expectation and are both cavalier about the whole thing, just pushing on as ever to the next goal. The more she succeeds, the more she needs him, the more important she becomes in his life as a joyful product of their common striving.

Gabe

Gabe believes in girls' athletics and in those he works with, and he particularly believes in Candy. Candy's relay win is a typical high for him that brings no surprises. To this day no one at Jefferson has exceeded Candy's time that day nor the relay record, so she remains unchallenged. This is something runners like Gabe live for as coaches, for their teams and for themselves. Years later, Sheila sought out Gabe to thank him again for his work that helped the relay team place so high at the LA City Championship that year. This is better than the vegan sandwiches he lived for then and still does today. Recently, he finished second in the 2018 LA Mt. Baldy Race in his age category, 65-and-over. The bond with Candy in 1980 was, as ever, about the common joy of work and runners' passion.

Summertime and the Livin' Is Easy—

There were seductive conversations in the summer of 1980. Talk between people who work together Monday through Friday often betrays a raw and earnest candor not even found at home or among friends. Working in a select group toward a common goal ups the ante, producing blatantly confident probes, revelations, secrets and empathetic stroke responses. We know it's more interesting to check in with the work team than to read the tabloids. A setting stocked with teenagers and those hired for their ability to relate to them is even more palpable. Such was the setting at Jefferson in the summer of 1980.

It was unduly quiet, vacant and hot all over campus. The irony of quiet in the middle of LA during the glorious vacation season was downright seductive. On these and other effects we might lay the guilt of Candy's cheekiness in 1980 summer school. She is one person who never takes a break and who is already somewhat giddy with success at a young age, student summer assistant to Mr. Robinson in Math, set for athletic and academic scholarships, and cautiously friendly with her running coach.

It is amazing to hear Juana flat out ask Candy about herself and Mr. Grosz, though many surely had brought it up by now. It's more amazing that Candy quizzes Gabe about his own dating. Phenomenal but indicative of what is about to happen between them is Candy's casual, sudden prediction that they will become a couple. Candy recorded the key innuendos of that hot summer in her documentation of quiet little moments which open the doors to a somewhat historic love/ sex/legality predicament. Make no mistake. We are dealing with two virgins here, both of abnormally high character, who are nonetheless, in the swim of the West Coast semi-tropical season, thrown the fisherman's hooks of . . . is it joy, risk, or both?

Candy's Recorded Conversation from Summer 1980

Juana is chatting with Candy at their side by side lockers.

Juana: "My folks already have my entire summer planned. I wish once we'd go somewhere besides Lake Arrowhead. I think I could find my way around the lake in the dark, I've been there so many times."

Candy: "My parents never want to go anywhere since we moved here. In their minds, LA's the last stop. I'm going to work for extra credit this summer and hopefully graduate early."

Juana: "Have you applied yet?"

Candy: "Yeah, to Mr. Robinson in the Math Department."

Juana: "He's pretty cool. Hope you get it."

They close their lockers and walk to the main door leading out.

Juana: "This is going to sound off the wall, but do you have a thing for Coach Grosz?"

Candy: "It doesn't sound off the wall."

Juana: "Well, do you?"

Candy: "Come on, Juana. That would be crazy."

Juana nods: "It sure would be."

The girls, in a bubbly aura of gossip, move on to other subjects and exit the building.

What's interesting here is, first, Juana's insistence on asking the question twice and second, Candy's answering twice and contradicting herself. First, she says the question of affection for Gabe is not "off the wall." Then she says even mentioning it is crazy. Clearly, if there is a line drawn between young female Black students and their young male White coaches, and we all know there is, she's somehow beginning to ride that line, at least in her inner feelings. Athletes, new or seasoned, are on average less tempted to waste their energy and focus in unrewarding corridors. For Candy, however, the athletic commitment that might have filled up her feelings is inextricably and warmly connected to the man.

Others are overly relaxed that summer. Candy recorded daily trivia shared with Gabe in his classroom on his lunch break. It's in good taste to save developing friendship at school for break time, but crossing ethical lines between teachers and students happens there as well. There's no safe zone.

She started stopping by Gabe's room regularly on break, as did a lot of people, and the chummier they all got, the more Candy rattled on like a typical teenage girl, playing with hypotheses and images bouncing around her head. Gabe, who never thought of himself as someone who should spend time alone, rattled back at all players, never closing his classroom door and comfortably responding to almost anyone. Even other teachers join the fray.

Candy's records of the time open with Gabe, as ever, grabbing an avocado sandwich. He's simultaneously eyeing a lot of paraphernalia taken out of his cabinets to sort, and he's in a state of disorder and decides to think it over while munching on food. A radio in the background plays the Coasters singing "Poison Ivy," a warning song, sung to men, about getting involved with women. Candy bounces in and spouts "Boo!" And Gabe jumps, startled.

"Did I scare you?" she asks.

"Does Mr. Robinson know you're here?" He checks back.

This makes Candy only laugh and repeat her question: "Well, did I scare you, Mr. Grosz?"

"Would it make you happy if I said yes?" he responds.

"Yes," she plays on.

"Then, no," he blurts deadpan without even looking up at her.

Candy stays on her inane topic. She knows they're friends, that it's summer, breaktime, and no matter how mature he is, she's a happy, pretty girl with all the rights of a happy, pretty girl on a lackluster summer day. She pulls a desk up close and sits down.

"I did so scare you," she adds. "Don't deny it. I saw you jump."

He mumbles back at her, blandly, not even looking at her face. "No. That was just a nervous reaction." He feigns a twitch next, which implicates himself in the whole aura of summer and helps him appreciate that it's summer school, when there aren't enough unattended class details to ruin your break. "See, there it goes again," he says, acting like somebody on *Saturday Night Live*.

"Oh, you lie," Candy acts out.

"No, I'm serious," he says, with a final sickly twitch.

"Grosz, you're so weird," finally makes him laugh before plunging into his sandwich first and then back to the paraphernalia.

"How's that summer work in the Math Department?" asks Gabe.

"It's all right. Mr. Robinson has the jazz station on all day. I love that cool music. He plays Ella and Billie."

Candy's brain lapses into memories of "Blue Moon," heard this morning and "Dream a Little Dream" yesterday.

Blue Moon

You saw me standing alone—
Without a dream in my heart—
You knew just what I was there for
Someone I really could care for—

Stars shining above you
Night breezes seem to
Whisper I love you
Birds singing in the sycamore trees
Dream a little dream of me.

At this point, Candy opens her pointed inquisition in a cute and perky teen fashion: "By the way, thanks for the post-card you sent all of us from Yosemite. Who did you go with?"

"A couple of friends."

"Guy friends or girl-friends? Why not girl-friends?"

"Because I don't have any."

"Why not?"

"I just don't."

"Are you gay?"

Gabe snickers, "No, Candy. I'm not. Enough with the questions!"

"My mother says you're a homosexual."

"But I've never even met your mother. "

"That one Saturday after we finished our run at Griffith Park and you dropped me off—she asked me—since you spend so much time with the team, do you have a girl friend or a wife? I told her all I know is that you visit your mother on Sundays, and she said, 'That figures.'"

Candy looks over the stuff on Gabe's desk, and her eyes land on a framed *Sports Illustrated* Jim Ryun cover photo. "Who's that?

"That's Jim Ryun, one of the greatest runners ever. He was the first high school kid to run the mile in under four minutes, and he later broke the world record. He's one of my favorites."

"Wow, that's neat!"

"You want it?"

"You would give it to me?"

"It's yours. Take good care of it."

"Are you sure?"

"I want you to have it. You're a great athlete. He's a great athlete. You belong together."

"You're a great coach, Mr. Grosz. Listen, I can't stay long. Mr. Robinson is going to get suspicious. I think he knows about us."

"What's there to know?"

"That I've been coming here all summer. And every time I come back he says, 'How's Mr. Grosz?'"

"I think you'd better go."

She cradles the framed picture and leaves, with "Oh, see you tomorrow."

The conversations narrow in a mood like the mating dance of buzzing bees. The Summer 1980 conversations at Jefferson High were almost as lazy and lame as songs from the Black opera, Porgy and Bess:

> Oh, I've got plenty o' nuttin
> And nuttin's plenty for me.
> I got no car, got no mule
> Got no misery.

Though we're told familiarity breeds contempt, summer school sweet rants at Jefferson breed mostly extreme levels of cheekiness. A peppy competition pops up between Candy and a pretty sub teacher for Gabe's attention. Gabe had only a handful of dates in his life, and never the same woman twice. The more these women try, the more he knows—it's not going to happen. Knowing he will not date the sub a second time and intending never to date his student, he barely looks them in the eye as they flaunt their wiles.

Candy now knows a bit about Gabe's dating life, or non-dating life as is the case. But so does a pretty blond summer-sub who's already on his notorious one-date-only list. And neither of them is giving up on earning his attention. Neither for a single minute believes he has any interest at all in the other. It's this kind of confidence that aids women in a history of phenomenal success with men.

There are always only two people in the story from the viewpoint of the seductress.

One drudging day at break time in July, Paula, the very pretty late-20's blond sub, edges into Gabe's always public classroom with a stapler in her pretty hand and opens with a sort of May West line: "Hey there, stranger. I haven't seen you in a while."

This causes Gabe to snap to, with almost the same alertness he'd have shown if he needed to call for a security guard. A lot of students waltz in and out of his room but not many female teachers. Candy glances over her shoulder, but Paula doesn't seem to notice her. She offers him the stapler with a soft personalizing smile.

"I thought you might want this back."

Gabe tries to reclaim the stapler, but Paula doesn't let go. She stops to flirtatiously stroke his hand. Candy watches the display and studies Gabe's reaction as Paula finally let's go.

"Uh, thanks, Paula.

"How was your summer, Gabe?"

"It was all right."

"Did you do anything special that didn't involve running?"

"Well, I spent a week at Yosemite."

"Really. I heard it's magnificent. Who'd you go with?"

"Just a couple of friends."

"Maybe we can go together sometime."

Candy knows what's going on. She snickers under her breath, and Gabe glances at her and then back.

"We'll see."

"Great. Remember, don't be a stranger."

Paula strolls to the door, gives Gabe a come-on look over her shoulder, and leaves.

At this, Candy starts giggling. "Gee. I think she likes you."

"What?"

"Can't you tell when somebody likes you, Grosz?"

"Sometimes."

"You think she's pretty?"

"Yeah. I guess."

"You think I'm pretty?"

"Sure. You're pretty," he says uneasily.

"Who is she? I've never seen her?"

"She's a substitute teacher. We went out once. I never called her back. I just let it go."

"Mr. Grosz, you're tragic, but I'm glad you didn't call her back."

"Why do you say that?"

"Because she's not your type."

"What's my type?"

"Someone with everything. Beauty, brains, and talent. Someone like me."

"The next time I run into someone like you, I'll ask her out."

"You'll never find anyone like me. When's the last time you went out on a date?"

"I don't know. A while. Are you going to stop grilling me now?"

"How old are you?"

"How old do you think I am?"

"Somewhere in your late 20's."

"Close."

"It doesn't seem like you've ever been with a woman. If you know what I mean."

"That's no concern of yours!"

"I've never been with anybody."

"Nothing wrong with that."

"Do you ever think of getting married?"

"No. It doesn't cross my mind."

"Well, Mr. Grosz, one day I'm going to marry you."

This being the most exaggerated piece of gossip of the entire summer, Gabe is totally blown away. Candy, true to all her mighty exits, leaves on a play of force. She gets up, goes to the door, and gives him the Paula look over her shoulder. She laughs and walks out.

Complications Begin to Take a Toll

The first day of fall 1980 creeps in on the quick feet of silent runners. There seems to be no break, just a sudden blink of a time-lapse between the crazy, lazy summer program and the madhouse of fall enrollment, halls and locker rooms full of perspiring and dirt-dusted athletes and gym kids unable to stop talking long enough to find their lockers and rooms. Teachers stationed in the halls to help try to shout directions over the buzz are hopeless in detangling the masses before the first bell rings.

In the middle of this chaos Gabe hears over the P.A. system that he is expected to stop by Mr. Hayes' office, the principal's office, before leaving campus today. The students hear this too, and it's hard to say who's more curious about it. Juana and Candy discuss the threat, mentioning that a call to see Hayes has never been good news. Juana thinks Candy might know what's up, but Candy in her self-possessed way, thinks it has to be about her.

She moans, "Hayes probably is going to tell Grosz I can't run hurdles."

It's hard to imagine anyone would want to monitor Gabe, the most successful and probably best-loved teacher on campus. As for summer school loose talk, if "what goes down in Vegas stays in Vegas," surely what goes down during Jefferson summer school ought to stay in Jefferson summer school?"

Dream on, Gabe thinks, punishing himself for relaxing too much with his runners.

At 3:30, once the mayhem of the first day is over, he sprints across campus to administration, trying to act casual and normal, but facing a simultaneous put-down argument between two parts of himself in the background of his brain. It's not my fault everything these students say around here is out of line. Who knows how to dialogue with these kids? I'm good at it. And they produce. They respect me and they like me. That may be unusual, but it works. Candy hung out too much last summer, but that doesn't mean anything.

His inner voice sounds like thunder. He has to hear it, but now he has to stop listening. He is standing in the administration office, and colleagues are coming and going. He knows better. No one should speak or even think like that. Calmly and back in his own well-established role, he enters silently with a warm handshake for Hayes and an earnest expression of interest in what Hayes has to say.

Gabe sits down, and Hayes puts his work aside. His mood is suddenly grave. He's got something important to say, and Gabe senses it.

"Close the door and have a seat, Mr. Grosz."

This is a bad start. Gabe would rather not close the door and is never called Mr. Grosz, even in administration. He feels like replying, "Sure, Alvin," but realizes that's what the cheeky students would do under the circumstance and not what he should do. Maybe Hayes is right; maybe the students have been influencing him too much. He already has developed a profound ability to "get" what they're saying and to satirize staff, in fact of course, himself.

Hayes sees that both are formally seated and his papers are set aside for him to lean full-arm on the desk and directly at Gabe. "I've asked to see you because I need to discuss a couple of things I've personally observed and a few of your athletes have commented to me about."

At this, Gabe suddenly thinks he knows what the issue may be—Candy! She'd recently pressured him to work a lot extra with her off the field. Both he and she know it would be worth it for them, the team ,and the school. She is the kind of athlete who anywhere else would get special training no one else could give her at Jefferson. He knows what he can say to Hayes about it, but he also knows it's starting some jealousy among other girl runners.

"First, I'd like to congratulate you on a successful season. In your first year as head coach of girls' track you've developed a positive rapport, and most of them seem to like what you're doing."

At this, Gabe cracks an uneasy smile, thinking about why Hayes says, "most of them."

"However, it has come to my attention that you're spending a lot of time with one athlete in particular, specifically, Candy Mills."

Without even thinking, Gabe—the master of response—replies, "I spend a lot of time with all my athletes, Mr. Hayes."

"That may be true, Mr. Grosz, but you spend quite a bit more time with Candy. Not only do you coach her in the afternoon, but you continue coaching her after the other athletes have gone home. On top of that, we've seen you two running every morning before school."

Gabe tries to intervene with, "Well, it's just…"

But Hayes is in courtroom mode, unable to accept the slightest interruption of statement of case. "Surely, she's a great athlete with lots of potential, great potential. And I can certainly understand you having a vested interest in her. But you simply cannot let her dominate your time. There are other athletes to consider. Just the other day, Dawn was in here, quite upset, telling me about the extra time you're spending with Candy."

This story wounds Gabe, who does believe he's in balance socially with the whole group, not to mention at great exhaustion to himself. We're talking about extra output here, he feels, and that means I'm doing extra—with everybody—which should be a feather in my cap, not something for Dawn to complain about.

But all he says is, "Dawn has never said anything to me."

Hayes, in the mode of the Wizard of Oz, booms out moralistic, benign-sounding comments, intended to limit Gabe's role. "Coaching a girls' team is a challenging endeavor, Mr. Grosz. You can't favor one athlete without the others feeling resentful. Girls take that kind of thing to heart."

As if this is news to him, Gabe humbly accepts the thought with "I'll keep that in mind, sir." This may be the first and last time any faculty at Jefferson called another "sir," but the term opens the door for the race card.

Clearing his throat, Hayes adds, "And another thing. Candy's a Black female and you're a White man. This is a Black community, and it doesn't look right for a White guy to be running through South Central alongside a Black girl. A lot of people around here have a problem with that."

In his never-failing naivete and boundless liberal spirit, Gabe senses this point to be unfair. He has a new millennium spirit in the twentieth century and should know you don't simply choose a 1980's inner-city job and assume every spot is happily integrated because you, for one, are in it. He blurts out, "But she's my athlete," with no forethought.

Hayes rebounds, "Yes, but the community doesn't know that. They only know what they see, and it doesn't look right." He lays down the law, the law of culture that threatens to doom our hero.

Luckily, Gabe responds, "I understand," though he does not understand.

This is the crucial moment when society first confronts Candy and Gabe with a clear statement of deeply set cultural law violated. It's a theory here and not an exact accusation. But we wonder how Gabe will stand up to it and how he will get Candy to do the same. A sense of us and them emerges for the first time in his mind. How will we deal with this? How will they?

Since Hayes is a very nice guy, busy having to at the moment take down another very nice guy, he reduces the threat level in closure: "I've been a principal for many years, Gabe, and I've seen a lot. I'm sure your relationship with Candy is strictly appropriate and professional. I'm not suggesting otherwise. You're her coach and I can understand there's a natural bond there. Just be careful not to let anything problematic take place. Do you understand?"

"Well, nothing's going to happen, I assure you," Gabe says.

But deep inside, those words are not quite swallowed whole. Though they've been the farthest thought from his mind, now they hold the silent power to open Pandora's box of what can happen or at least of what others may perceive. How Gabe interprets Hayes and his own responses is crucial, but what he says may not be what he really thinks.

Once outside Hayes' office, the first person Gabe sees is Candy exiting the hall with Juana. She also knows of this administrative meeting and seems distracted, but remarkably, she says nothing.

Proof of the Pudding— They're a Dream Team, 1981

If there were no success, this would be a bland story, but Candy and Gabe bubble in success, causing them like Disney characters to ride above the fray in glitter and song. They trust themselves in a depressed community where few do. They cannot change their path because they are well on it already. They cannot avoid intrigue, emotion, pressure, or obsession because they are successful, and these are by-products of success. Like a lot of highly successful people, they will be tempted to rest on their laurels and break rules. The success keeps pouring in, and so will the temptation.

Candy's successes immediately prove even more outstanding in the hurdles than at her medley relay. The 1981 Girls' 330-yard Hurdles Meet, held at Jefferson this time, is set up for a staggered start of 330-yard low hurdles. In the visitors' seats, parents and fans cheer for their Washington High School track team who wear red and black.

Gabe stands on the home side of the track in front of seats filled with Jefferson parents and fans. Candy, wearing her kelly-green and gold track suit, takes her place at the start line. Three girls from Washington kick out and plant their feet at the starting blocks. The starter bellows," Runners to your marks!" The girls, bent to the task in a nervous row, set eyes on the track, and the gun goes off.

Candy bolts to the front, but she clips the second hurdle and goes down, crashing hard to the track. This opens things for the three girls from Washington, who quickly clear the hurdle and start to take the lead. In the next instant, Candy rolls back onto her feet and gets it going again. She strides over the third hurdle and then the fourth and fifth, almost as if they weren't there. But without them we wouldn't experience the athletic finesse of a star. She passes one runner, then another, and the third on the final straightaway. She crosses the finish line in first place. The crowd goes wild, and Principal Hayes is beside himself.

Gabe trots across the infield to Candy and shows her his stopwatch, and she beams as she sees the time—44.5 seconds, a new school record and the fastest time by any LA City hurdler. This is a new record for Jefferson. She wipes off with a clean towel, oblivious to the scrapes on her arms and legs from the fall. In her preparation for the Washington race, Gabe and Candy had set a goal for her to run under 50 seconds. She makes the best hurdling time in the city, and the scores keep improving as she practices.

As of today, no one at Jefferson has bettered Candy's hurdle times or the story of her Washington race. In her next race, Candy beats Ms. Hunter of Dorsey High who won the California State Championship the previous year. Candy's 44.5 is tied for the second fastest high school hurdle time in the US.

So temptation sets in for everybody. After this fabulous moment in Jefferson High history, it's as if all bets are off, all goals, regimens, practice sessions, and pressure. The whole team looks as if they took one deep breath of relief. Gabe's girls are giggling and screaming, "You cool." "You great." "Yo—first." "Hey, damn the MAN!" and every other happy thought the girls ever wanted to smear their opponents with.

"Come on, Grosz," says Anthony. "You're up for a night with the younger generation. You're gonna shove popcorn at the Cineplex with us. We gotta see *Airplane*."

Neal adds, "Unless you got a date."

Erwin imitates Grosz, pointing a bony finger at them with "Gosh, darn it, Neal. Show some respect."

Neal shows full agreement, bending over and tapping his butt cheeks, "I got yo respect right here, nigga."

What can Gabe do? He feels even mightier than they do, more finished for the night, more proven, and more ready for a movie.

"Sure, guys, sure," he says, folding into the crowd that falls into two cars and launches off screeching down the road. The marquee is tempting with four hits at one time: *The Shining, The Blues Brothers, Superman II,* and *Airplane.* Minutes later they're all sunken into their stiff velvet seats, including Anthony, Neal, Tyrus, Dawn, and Juana, with Candy squeezing in next to Gabe on the end. The team is beyond tired, blinking to keep their eyes open.

Candy puts the popcorn bucket under her seat, notes the nearly empty theater, and leans into Gabe and whispers, "I'm tired, Grosz."

She is tired the way only a winner can be, ready to retire to college or something, ready to put her head on his shoulder. She rests it there silently, and Gabe doesn't dare to move. It's uncomfortable and new for him, after five first dates in ten years and no seconds. He shoots a side-glance at the others who seem also half-asleep. For the first time in his life he relaxes with a girl. He feels blanketed in the track "family," hypnotized by trust and good luck. He takes to her warmth and closeness, and it feels strange but right.

Later he pulls his 1967 sedan up across the street from Candy's house, a modest stucco cottage on Lima Street right near school. It's dark and feels late because it's the end of a tiring day full of accomplishment. No one is around except owls making long sweet hollow sounds. The moon makes everything look luminous and beautiful. Candy and Gabe are resting in spirit together for the first time, dropping the tension of being a girl and a man, a hurdler and a coach, screaming out inwardly, "We're only Candy and Gabe, and it feels so much better." They know now that they were always a perfect match forced to pretend they were not.

Candy, of course, breaks the exquisite silence. "Do you like me, Mr. Grosz? I mean, more than a coach would an athlete?"

His defenses down, Gabe takes her face between his hands and looks her in the eyes. "I shouldn't be telling you this, but I do. I've been feeling it the last couple of weeks."

They breathe free in that dark, quiet, special moment, and hold hands.

"Why didn't you tell me before?" she asked.

"I think it's wrong. You're only 17 . . . I'm your teacher and your coach." He was not confessing, not backing off, but stating a fact with all the varied emotions the fact puts on the table.

"It doesn't matter," she says, suddenly returning to her adamant self-assured stamina. The confessions wake her up out of the mellow night dream they are in. "I've had feelings for you for a while, and it's not a schoolgirl crush," she softly finishes.

For all the sense of newness and release to the night, both statements also feel irrevocable, as if there were nothing else that needs to be said, . . . ever. They both smile at this, but don't say anything else. It is like a secret formal proposal of marriage, no ring or party needed, held all in whispers. They were, in the moment, like two ancient Eastern pilgrims, not new souls, but old souls that already know their fate.

At this, Candy exits silently, and goes to the front door and opens it with her key. It is her easiest departure ever. For her, the inquietude has finally passed. Tonight, her heart at least is at peace.

The Shit Hits the Fan. Where Is This Going?

High schools have almost no Pandora's box in which to hide secrets. Even things you don't yet know about yourself, your homies do. Candy and Gabe discretely seek solace and support from their friends who seem to have already thought over the issue of what could quickly mount to statutory rape. Long before Hester Prynne is torturously forced to wear the infamous "scarlet letter," everyone knows it is forthcoming. Candy could lose Gabe if they knowingly consummate their love, and Gabe could be stigmatized leading to the destruction of his career and reputation, and a long jail time. But no one seems blinded from these facts but them. Even today, almost 40 years later, Gabe says, "But it was all for love" with the full naivete that implies, as if the court system would ever consider good will in determining a statutory rape verdict.

Candy Talks to Neal

Personal stories aside, Jefferson's track and field continues to gain. Shortly after Candy's two sensational meets, the boys' two-mile race sees Tyrus take first place. Off the track, Candy corners Neal with her secret and walks him off to an empty field.

"Let's just keep walking," she says. "It'll look like we're warming down."

"Hey, what's up?" he asks. "I don't wanna know no secrets, okay?"

"Well, it's not going to be a secret between us," she rants. "I've got something to tell you, but you have to promise it won't go any further than right here. Promise first," she demands.

"So what's it I'm not supposed to tell anybody?" Then, with a defeated sense that there's no stopping Candy, whether she's doing the right thing or the wrong thing, he says, "Promise? Yeah, yeah, I promise."

She takes an index card from her sweatshirt pocket and hands it to him. "Remember? You promised. Read it."

Neal reads the card aloud: "Good luck. Love, Gabe."

Candy studies him for the slightest reaction. "Cool, but who the hell is Gabe?"

Candy, a bit nervous for a response, shoves Neal in the shoulder. "Come on, Neal. Gabe's Mr. Grosz."

"Grosz wrote this?" He actually is stunned.

"He gave it to me yesterday," she adds, . . . after practice." She takes the card back from him and looks at it again herself.

"So what's with this love shit?" asks Neal, his voice a little spent and hoarse. "What the hell have you two been up to?"

"He loves me," she finally admits it—to someone—to Neal.

He says, "Did he tell you that? In so many words?" Neal's now serious and digging, playing bad cop. "How long has this been going on?"

Candy, unsure whether to be proud or guilty, simply states, "About two weeks."

Now Neal is so loud, she's glad she hauled him off to the outskirts of the campus. "Girl, you're under 18, and that makes you jailbait. He can go down for it. . . . I'm talking about PRISON!"

But Candy's adamant. "You can't go to jail for loving someone."

This unglues the more street-smart Neal. "Girl, you're livin' in a dream world. Don't you know anything?"

Candy, always in control and not the tearful type, persists, despite a whiny female projection of why-don't-you-understand-me? "Well, we're getting married after I turn 18."

Neal, in astonishment, quizzes emotionally. "Does Grosz know that?"

Candy merely smiles coyly. "Not yet."

This leaves Neal leaning all to one side, talking to himself now. "Grosz? Gonna marry the under-age hurdler from New York?" He keeps shaking his head and saying, "That man's crazy!"

"Neal," she pleads, "you don't know what you're talking about.

"No, Candy, you don't know what you're doing. You're both crazy! . . . Wait, did you have sex?"

Candy says nothing, but her face tells the whole story.

Neal straightens up to the task. "Man, I don't . . .Do you love the dude?"

Candy, at this, looks around the yard, at her feet, and finally at Neal. "Yeah, I do."

"This is way over your head, girl," he says, totally firm.

"I can handle it," she replies as she always does to everything.

"You need a tee-shirt that says that. One of these days it's not gonna be true anymore. Damn, you guys are gonna do the ring and the 'I do' thing?"

"Wanna come?" Candy asks him sincerely, with the sense that not a whole lot of people will.

"Come where?" Neal drones painfully through her announcements.

"To our wedding," Candy says.

"Candy," Neal addresses her like a father asked to accept Gabe as a fiancé, "There ain't gonna be no wedding."

"Come on, Neal, what do you mean?"

"Cause your mother's gonna kill you—you and Mr. Grosz! No, there ain't gonna be no wedding…. but there surely gonna be a funeral and a burial."

"You don't know what my mother will do."

Neal's insight is astounding, and so is his answer to this one: "She's Black, ain't she? That's all I need to know." He shakes Candy's hand and says, "Well, it was nice knowing you."

Seasoned competitor that she is, she slaps his hand away with a final "Cut it out, Neal."

He looks at her a long look and returns to Neal-the buddy. "I won't tell, you know, but sooner or later it's gonna come out, and all hell's gonna break loose."

She begs him, "Not if you don't tell."

"Oh yeah?" he returns. "It won't make no difference. Y'all playing with fire, and it's only a matter of time til you get burnt."

Miraculously, Candy leaves him at that, unwilling to turn her moment of joy into an endless argument. They kick a few sticks and toss a few stones on the way back to the locker rooms, then engage in a game of silence. As they start to run into students again and see each passing face one by one, they think about how things are going to change, how each person will see Gabe and Candy differently. They see a party where the balloons are burst.

Candy and Mom

Hours later Candy feels the first soft winds of Spring 1981 wafting down her block and sweeping across South Central at sunset. It's the kind of thing a young girl in love notices. The exquisite reality of being in a love relationship with Gabe and the warm air and pink aura make her want to dance, enjoy it, talk about it, and see Gabe even more. She's singing to herself on the comfy porch with the glider, watching the colors change all along the horizon, oranges, rose, then purple. The soft spring nights on her street always remind her of the Dunbar Jazz Club that was nearby in the 30's, the one she and her mom always talk about. She has fantasies of going there, with Gabe, dancing, of singing there as a star herself, of turning all the school jerk talk into bluesy song, so everybody she knows is moaning sweetly together. She sings louder and louder, slower and slower, and deeply. She's a profound singer, and she has something to sing about.

Anything would be better than having to bottle up all her joy and deny it every day. She's not in an era when a millennial therapist is going to hold her while she cries and listen to her needs, help her map out a way to plan and space this unlivable relationship.

All the fuck'n Niggas are set out to go berserk and start a riot, if we even hold hands around here, she's thinking. *The White world's set to stop this case in its tracks, so we'll stay the first and last Black-White couple around here. The school board's going to reverse civil rights and throw us both out of the system, us and all the successes we bring them.*

Somehow the sinking beauty of their story enflames her heart and she continues to sing right there, leaning on the glider and staring at the sunset. Unlike Romeo and

Juliet, she and Gabe are leaders, she thinks. *We can stand anything. Romeo and Juliet destroyed themselves by trying to hide. We're not like that.* All down the street you can hear her singing her blues songs. She moans deeply and loudly:

> *Ni—ight just feels ri—ight*
> *An' he/so close to me*
> *I only/wanna be—*

At this, Delois comes out, closing the front screen door carefully not to make a sound, not to surprise anyone but to reverence the song. Candy sings it well, reminding her mom also of the jazz club they so often recall dreamily from their grubby, forgotten neighborhood.

"Candy, you're still write'n the Blues!" Delois says, putting both of her hands over her heart. "You gotta write down the words as they come to you, right now."

Candy stops, looking at her mother for the first time as the most complex puzzle she ever had to solve. Of course, she'll love my songs, but I can't let her catch the words. "Night just feel right, Mommy."

"That's beautiful, honey, but don't make'm love songs, cause you ain't date'n, and yer too young for love songs. I know you want a great teacher one day like Mr. Grosz, but you'll get there in time and find another teacher just like him. After school, after you finish all your school'n, you may just be a teacher yourself and find another one just like'm."

Candy cannot go back to more fake talk, more jerk talk, not til at least the sun goes down. Instead she just continues singing, while Delois gets pen and paper and writes the words down as they come out. Candy sings instead now about her mom, knowing her story is just as harsh as her own:

Pretty in Black

She woke up every morning/filled with some uncertainty.

Upon her head she wore a crown/of nappy dignity.

Written under Candy's writer name, Billie, for her mom

"That's beautiful, Baby, really beautiful. I'm go'in in now. You just watch your father tonight. Every night, you just send him back if he starts walk'n in the middle of the night, okay? The ladies are just runn'n this house. We'll be fine, if we're jus runn'n this house." Delois always speaks with conviction and even more so when she is especially tired. Spring makes her feel restful, like wanting to go lie under a tree. She has suspicions about Candy, Gabe, the school board, and her husband, but she's tired, yet wants to believe somehow in all of them.

Gabe and His Friend

The breeze and exquisite sunset make Candy want to sing, waft her jazz dramatically across the Wilshire Corridor and its famous LA Country Club 15 miles north of her ghetto to where Gabe usually has his sunset run. In 1981, runners were not allowed to enter club grounds, but that does not deter Gabe and his friend. That's where and when the two first start running along the edges of the course. It's an off-hour and no social life emerges even near the course. It seems a perfect time to break and talk.

Jon, White and in his 30's, has never faced the kind of intense work relationships Gabe has. He's never worked in a rowdy setting with young adults who crave attention and need role models. He's never run closely with young female athletes. But Gabe loves this guy, who's becoming a psychiatrist, and hopes he'll have some empathy for his maddening state of love that's going to be hard to explain to anyone.

"Your ego's slipping," Jon says. "You're apologizing for everything today, so what did you do that's worth apologizing for? I know when you're feeding on some fixation and can't get real."

"I wish it were just a fixation," Gabe admits. "It's crazy love. I'm in love."

This makes Jon laugh; Gabe's so cute.

"Don't laugh. Love can be one of the worst crises ever," Gabe moans.

"Come on," says Jon.

"No, really. I never knew any women well, and this one's not quite a woman yet, and this is real, important, big, everything. It's bigger than me. I don't even understand it, but I am not going to deny it. I've never been in love before. I might never fall in love again. I never even thought about it before."

"Well," Jon tries to placate Gabe's state in a therapeutic tone, "There's nothing wrong with love, no matter how it feels."

"I'm afraid there is, in my case." Gabe begins to let the whole thing out. "I'm in a situation that's over my head. I don't know how to handle it. Maybe you can give me some advice. I'm always the advice-giver, but not this time."

"What's going on, Gabe?" Jon now appreciates his training and goes into practice mode.

Gabe struggles to tell enough while kicking up crunchy white stones all along the path, without making notes, without even beginning to understand himself. What's happened or how? He stops and sits down in the thick and fragrant grass, getting Jon to do the same and looks him in the eye. With a focus Gabe has never before given the subject, he starts, "You remember Candy, don't you?"

"Sure," Jon says, "the hurdler. What about her?"

"I think I'm in love." Gabe admits this, acting like so many guilty court subjects accused of showing no expression and no remorse. He's just going to sit there and take it, no matter what his best friend thinks.

"In love with one of your athletes?"

Jon thought he knew his friend, but he'd never picked up on the slightest hint of this. He's clearly confronting a career problem, while Gabe's pouring out his heart in a sad personal story, and n'er these two friends shall meet!

Gabe continues, "I told her how I feel."

"Gabe, we've been friends a long time, and I've never known you to be in love with anyone."

Jon is the one in denial here and has completely thrown his therapist skills out the window. Back on the story, Gabe answers only, "It's my first time, Jon."

"But the girl's only what, 17? She doesn't exactly qualify as a woman."

Jon is obviously unlikely to fall in love or even understand such a thing, especially since he doesn't seem to know that everyone is in love with 17-year-old girls and they're the ones who define womanhood for the rest of us. The teeter-totter battle for weight is set on even balance.

We have the story, an emotional mess, and reality, an even more serious mess. Is this a matter for empathy or for rage? Jon is seeing his friend dig a hole and get inside. He has no intention of chatting about what it feels like in the hole. He wants to pull his friend out, and right now.

But Gabe is blubbering with lovesickness. "All I know is, I've never had feelings like this."

Jon remains steady with, "Look. I understand there's an emotional connection you haven't experienced before. But, if you pursue this relationship, not only are you going to get hurt, but she will too. A teacher-student relationship is doomed from the start."

"I know I'm crossing the line, Jon, but I didn't plan it."

"Just don't let your emotions sabotage your rational thinking."

Jon's point is excellent, but he drops the opportunity to question Gabe's whole defense of "falling" in love (unplanned), as though he has no responsibility in the love affair.

"So, what do you suggest I do?" Gabe begs, cornering his friend who's getting up because one leg has fallen asleep.

Struggling to his feet in more ways than one, Jon ends the session exactly as no artful therapist would, in loud proclamation suggesting his words are the last words, and there can be no valuable point to ever follow from Gabe: "You need to put an end to it. If you can't do that, at least wait until she's 18. If you really love her, and she loves you, then you'll be together."

This is a watershed moment for Gabe and Jon. They are no longer the boyhood friends they were, because today each is compelled to act like a man to himself and to each other. They've never faced anything this dangerous to their friendship. They also fail to hear each other well enough, and neither comes to understand the other. What does not happen between them this evening has the power to change things forever. Dusk covers them in warm hues and breezes of yesteryear, but their issue halts them in time. They cannot leave in the same harmony they brought with them, and they are both unsettled about Gabe's future.

Candy and Gabe

These are the moments in Candy and Gabe's story that contradict their intelligence and discipline. Where are their strengths when they need them, in Gabe's conversation with Jon and Candy's with her friend and with her mother? Gabe fails to reply to Jon's sound advice, and Candy fixates dreamily about a wedding while told the same thing by Neal. She also fails to confide in the earnest mother who loves her, setting up room for miscommunication that may trap her later.

One thinks of the free-spirited novice Maria in *The Sound of Music*. The nuns sing, "How do you solve a problem like Maria?" and answer their question with another question. "How do you hold a moonbeam in your hands?" Dealing with imprudent love is workable in a practical way for most but remains an inflexible matter of the heart-only for Candy and Gabe. They can only see through the eyes of love.

CHAPTER THREE

When the Chickens Come
Home to Roost

Out of the bag, the scandal automatically begins to brew its own history. Everyone who knows tells someone who tells someone else. Of course, Principal Hayes detects the heat and is forced to play his Nazi card. Of course, Candy's parents become the "parents from hell," insane and violent; that's their job. Jefferson High, girls' track, and the neighborhood in general succumb to something akin to the fall of Rome. In the midst of what people call scandal and an atmosphere growing more wicked every day, the instigators are also the victims. Candy and Gabe continue their habitual runners' schedule and discipline, while forces are stirring all around them. But there is no anger, only confusion, among colleagues and friends. For team runners, output seems a little uneven and attitudes mildly testy, to such a degree that things begin to happen, things Candy and Gabe would never have predicted or worked to prevent.

Candy, sensing a change in the air, is edgy training at the UCLA Track and Field Stadium for the forth-coming Arcadia Invitational, the biggest national high school track meet. It bears for Candy no resemblance to home. It's a pristine facility with 30 rows of seating and all-weather Tartan tracks, the lanes lined in permanent white. Candy has never seen anything but bleachers, dirt tracks, and chalk lines. When Gabe escorts her to practice at the track where low-level hurdles are already set up, for reasons easy to guess, she's out of sorts. She throws an arrogant question on him as if she doesn't even know him, as if he's a UCLA ref. "So, what is it you expect me to do, Grosz? Run against the clock?"

Grasping for regularity with Candy, he first gives a big wave to Evelyn Ashford, the world's fastest woman and an Olympic champion, on the other side of the track, then answers in a predictable "Grosz-age." "I just thought you should get a feel for the track before the meet. Girls are coming from all over the country to compete."

"The more the merrier," Candy unloads, beginning to worry Gabe a bit. Then she adds to his angst by jogging 20yard s out and 20 yards back, concluding with, "Can I go now?"

"I wish you'd take this seriously," is all he can say.

Perhaps as a consequence of many issues on Candy's shoulders, she takes off, clears the first hurdle, and then the second, but at the third performs an unpredictable error of stepping around the hurdle to the inside, and she goes down.

Gabe runs across the infield and up to her. He bends down, inspecting the left foot with one hand. Candy winces with pain, and he helps her up and over to a vehicle. "No more UCLA practice for you. I'm taking you to the UCLA hospital!" In the car, he tries to unravel the mystery of her footwork at hurdle three. He begs her, "What was that? What were you doing?"

"I told you I didn't want to run hurdles today, Grosz," she answers.

"This is no joke," Gabe says more to himself than Candy. "We can't afford too many days like this," but before he can add more, his hand catches a tear slipping secretly down Candy's hardy and unforgiving face.

"Okay. We've got an injury here, and that's all that matters." He feels like holding her closely, the way not only a lover would, but a parent—a child. "Okay, Sweetie, we're almost there."

Candy could use a short hospital stay, but they release her abruptly with a broken foot. While she tries to sort out an aborted season in her mind and make peace with a cast and a pair of crutches, she realizes she has to call her mom. She needs a tension release, but she's now in a season of tension that's germinating and growing into whole crops of tension no one would want to be responsible for any part of.

"Hello, Ma? Huh? I'm at UCLA. No, the hospital. I broke my foot. No. I'm alright. It's just a stress fracture." She covers the receiver and whispers to Gabe, "She's upset."

Her mom seems to want a confession and points of guilt, so Candy tries to calm her. "Yeah, but it was all my fault. I didn't listen to Mr. Grosz and . . . I'm what?" She leans over and whispers to Gabe again, "She says I'm hard-headed."

Gabe smirks, thinking there's no disagreement there.

Candy continues to explain things to her mother with less and less success. She's juggling her aching foot, the huge crutches, her own disappointment, Gabe's feelings, and now her mother's. "Look Mom, I have to wear a cast for a couple weeks and miss the Invitational. That's all . . . Yeah. The coach is here. Maybe he can explain it to you."

Candy hands Gabe the phone, saying, "My mother wants to speak to you."

"Hello, Mrs. Mills. Yes, she broke her foot going around, instead of over, a hurdle. I know, I know. It's not the thing to do, but under the circumstances, she seems to be in good spirits . . . Mrs. Mills? . . . Mrs. Mills?" Gabe hangs up with deep concern.

"What was that all about?" Candy asks.

His answer is shockingly flat. "I'm not sure. She hung up."

At this, a pall sets in upon the already grim scene. Neither knows what to say to the other, and the same goes for everybody else. Candy now expects to not even run the Invitational. This means Jefferson will not be represented. Mrs. Mills' suspicion of Gabe feels validated. Gabe expects to be back in Hayes' office, and Candy, the young lady of dreams, has to somehow pull everybody out of it, while she hobbles back to the hood. "This is one practice that's over," Gabe announces with exhaustion.

The following Monday, Coach Johnson with his boys' team, and Gabe and the girls' team, are all assembled on the Jefferson field and they cumulatively validate Candy walking on crutches toward them. Everybody associated with the team has heard the bad news. It's just going to take a lot of drama to work it all through.

Candy and Her Mom

At home, Candy and her mom can no longer skirt the issue. Candy makes her bed, careful not to bump her cast, and begins alone in her room to sort out some of the burdens of the moment, when her mom, Delois, moves in on the first chance Candy's had to think.

"You better not be tak'n breaks right now, not with everything sink'n because of you. I need to talk to you, Baby."

Candy turns surprised. "It's about the meet. I know. I'll still make the City Finals, and that's what counts."

But Delois resets the topic. "It's not about that. It's about you and Mr. Grosz."

"What about me and Mr. Grosz?" Candy questions as always.

"Have you two had sex?" Delois has to know.

"What?" Candy asks, as she did Neal when he asked the same thing. In the 80's it was not ever good to admit to having sex. The question was always considered unfairly loaded.

"He's my coach, Ma," she answers, ever the debater and politician.

"You're spending a lot of time with him. You just can't be running all that time," Delois probes.

"We see a lot of each other, but we talk about things," is the best hedging Candy do.

Delois walks to her, sits her on the bed, and looks her dead in the face.

Candy's eyes fill with tears, and she blurts out: "I love him, Mom, and he loves me too."

Unfortunately, Delois is now beside herself, smothering her sobs with gnarled and over-worked hands. "I knew it! I knew it!" she sobs, racing out of Candy's room.

At this, mother and daughter are both unable to speak, and Candy finds herself alone again in her room with her realities, her history, and her stuff, a room filled with trophies, medals, ribbons, and now one tear-stained framed picture of Jim Ryun that Gabe gave her. She holds it as if it were a picture of Gabe and not Ryun and promises deep inside not to let others' emotions get to Gabe or herself, to say or do whatever it takes to marry him, to get people to understand there is nothing cheap or wrong about true love between innocent lovers.

Not only is Delois about to burst out of her motherly cocoon in the guise of Joan of Arc, ready to make war on moral enemies, but the next day Principal Hayes calls Gabe back into his office in his alternate persona as a mighty Black bureaucrat. Jefferson begins to see the other side of faces and what society feels must be done about illicit love. Gabe and Candy are illicit in so many ways that a variety of punitive measures naturally emerge. As a teacher, he must lose his job; as a White man, he must exit the Black community; as a 29-year-old with a 17-year-old, he is suspected of other underage tendencies, which remain to this day the most damning accusation societies unleash.

Under the weight of all this, Gabe pulls up a chair in Principal Hayes' office. Hayes is visibly cranky when he lays out the accusation for which the only cure is to fire Gabe.

"I'll be straight with you, Mr. Grosz. Mr. and Mrs. Mills were in my office yesterday, and they were extremely upset. They claim you've been sexually involved with their daughter. Is this true?"

Gabe, the most honest and sincere man in the whole world, can only answer "Yes."

This is followed by Hayes, only hours ago, the most supportive of colleagues, begging for sanity with, "Man, do you realize what you've done?" Gabe's amazing reply gets Hayes out of his seat and pacing the room. "Boy, oh boy! You really got yourself in trouble now. Didn't I tell you to watch yourself, that something could happen? I should've never hired a young White man to coach the girls' track team! Now, I have no choice but to notify the Board of Education, and in this instance, you'll be placed on administrative leave."

"I didn't intend for all this to happen, Mr. Hayes," is Gabe's solemn conclusion.

"But it did, didn't it? I need you to pack up your things," Hayes demands, "and I advise you to keep away from Candy, and especially, keep your distance from Mr. and Mrs. Mills."

Hayes shakes his head in disappointment and sighs.

Gabe exits the office, slowly closing the door behind him.

There are lots of things wrong with a many-sided crime, so opinions and reactions to it are also many-sided. Cruelly, people did then and even now trust Gabe's intentions, however naive and poor his judgement was, while Candy was regularly viewed as a vixen over the love affair and scorned by her parents, many teachers and students. Reactions to their illicit love is the first real pressure in Gabe's life and threatens to be the straw that breaks the camel's back for Candy.

There's also a way their love is illicit and a way it's not. Both mothers denounce the union as a kind of racial disgrace, and Hayes is forced to deal with it as a representative of the Black community. Candy's teachers scorn her, and one presents her with her first "D." They read the union as a threat to their field. But in their small world, only the legal world criminalizes the age difference between 17 and 18.

Somehow, no one takes note of the prudence that holds these two together in a virtuous trust. Their love between themselves is sweet and true. Nonetheless, they are breaking sacred rules, and show no remorse due to a strange naivete' only lovers can fully understand. They are both dedicated to track with almost no social interests. Gabe, for instance, is literally 29, but socially and emotionally, he is a late bloomer. Those who know them together can see they are, in fact, two 17-year-olds. They are not out to make a racial statement or abuse their class contract as teacher and student. On the matter of age difference, she is a young, young-adult and he is a late young-adult. There is nothing about Gabe that fits a pedophilic lifestyle, nor is he promiscuous or ever married. Though hard to believe, Gabe never anticipated any problems over the relationship.

Nonetheless, Chicken Little's sky is falling in South Central in 1981. The next attempt of Candy and her mom to talk things through never has a chance. Delois walks again into Candy's room, but this second time it is to slap her. Her language is worse than Gabe's mother's is to him.

"You despicable slut! I brought you into this world, and I'll take you out! I should kill you, you little whore. If you'd murdered somebody, it'd be easier to deal with than sex with that White man!"

"I love him, Ma," Candy replies, barely audible and moving back and out of reach.

"What do you know about love? He doesn't love you," Delois continues on her rant.

"He's using you. All that man wanted was to have sex with a Black girl."

"He's not like that," Candy moans in defense.

"Yes, he is. He's exactly like that," Delois pounds. "He got what he wanted, and you let him have it. You were his little Black whore."

At this point the once invincible Candy falls helplessly into the nearest chair, her entire face wet with tears, unable to reply. She is being choked and notices her mom storm back out of the room, yelling in a new reign of terror.

"Your father's going to take care of that White bastard!"

At this, point, Candy stands to sudden attention as if Gabe is being attacked at that very moment. She pushes out a "Ma, no!" and falls back into her chair.

Time did tell of these abusive encounters behind closed doors on Lima Street. But no one knew for many years. The "fight or flight" in us all ran 98 percent "fight" for Candy. These personal family traumas at home, however, produced also two percent moments of desperately desired "flight," though the only person she really could've run to was Gabe, and he was the one she most refused to tell.

If this book were a film, we'd observe a reverent silence here to mark a life-changing period in Candy's life. Cameras would scan her multiple awards for school work and track, her blues lyrics stacking up on vari-colored note pad sheets, the porch lounge where she loved to sing, and the countless and endless runs with Gabe at her side both in competition and in their dawn runs before class.

At the end of that pause, cameras would catch her destabilizing the new choking feeling that the best is over and that she will have to resume flight stance just to stay sane. We'd see her resolve to hold what she had yesterday and live through a new life at the same time. As an optimist who always saw there is a will and a way, the climax of her tale is in this moment when she permanently commits to cowering to the penalties love with Gabe will bring.

Most love stories are warmer, full of beautiful love scenes that transcend the outside world. But Candy and Gabe have more in common with Romeo and Juliet, star-crossed lovers forewarned against being together. Even before legal threats ensue, both are sworn by authority figures on all sides never again to see each other or even talk to each other.

Where are counselors, ministers, and mediators of any kind to give understanding and support? Despite every member of the community holding an opinion and friends suggesting practical solutions, Gabe and Candy honestly have no one to discuss their intimacy with but each other. Gabe generally does not reach out to Candy because he's been told not to, but Candy continuously reaches out to Gabe, most often by phone, and he answers her lovingly, not just because he loves her, but because on a regular basis, she experiences abusive response from many and turns to Gabe for support.

Always the professional, he feels a void of discussion and resolution in his dismissal from Jefferson. Hayes is reliably fair enough, but many other principals would have brought Candy's parents together with Gabe to answer more questions and attempt to settle sides.

As is, no one is settled down. Despite losing his job and likely his future career, Gabe is the calm and most receptive person in all settings. But Candy can only mirror the excessive force she is receiving from so many. Though his students and team are a thing of the past, he never stops playing the role of the "good coach," even from the other side of the fence. He decides immediately after Hayes' dismissal that he should fill in the communication gap and talk to Candy's mother directly and carefully. He wants her to know the same thing he wants everyone to understand—that he and Candy are in love and intend to marry once it's workable. He does not know how worked up the Mills household is over the issue.

The very day of Gabe's dismissal, he pulls up in front of the Mills' house and parks. He walks to the front door and rings the bell. Delois barely pushes the front door open to see who it is, and Gabe squinches his head into that opening with a gentle and friendly: "Hello, Mrs. Mills."

"How dare you come to my house," she says, beginning immediately to close the door back in place.

"Please," says Gabe. "I didn't come here to upset you. I just came to talk to you about Candy and me."

At the thought of "Candy and me," Delois freezes, then steps out onto the porch and finally does close the door behind her. She does not offer a seat on the porch swing where Candy has written now so many love songs to him, where she has sung them out for her mother and passers-by to hear. Delois performs no common courtesy and does not sit down herself. They are alone at that moment and that spot, so she unloads exactly what is restraining her from being herself.

"I don't give a shit about anything you have to say about my daughter! If you want to talk to me, you should have talked to me before anything happened between you two."

Gabe listens harder than he ever has as a coach, an employee, harder than he ever listened as a kid to his own mother. His eyes are paralyzed in attention. He speaks softly "but" only enrages her more.

"You were too goddamn scared to talk to me, but you weren't too scared to have sex with my daughter, were you? Now you jus' get the hell outa here, Mr. Grosz, 'cause I have nothing to talk to you about."

In the one-second pause in which she blasts the last word into his eyes, Delois sees the expression of a 29-year-old facing the first real crisis of his life. A real man, he is there to defend, not only himself, but Candy, the altogether too young and inexperienced girl he loves.

"I love your daughter, Mrs. Mills. I had no intention of hurting her or anyone. I would never willingly do anything like that. We eventually want to get married."

Gabe apologizes desperately for what he believes deserves no apology. Applying the idea of marriage to what Delois sees as nothing but shame and scandal stops her on her feet, causing Gabe to enter his last thought, one he will regret for the rest of time. "You would like me too if you knew me," he throws out, a hopeless attempt at friendship.

Who knew that Delois, totally convinced of the evil of an older White man intimate with her young Black daughter, would misread his words? Showing the tired yellow whites of her eyes and backing up to her doorway in a seething sense of insult, she says, "Me too? You dare talk to ME like that? You belong in jail where you cannot hurt any of us. Get the hell off my property, you goddam White bastard!"

They both back away at this, each having shocked the other. And neither speaks to the other again, for years.

With Gabe off-campus and unemployed, Candy and Gabe under order not to meet, no daily morning jogs before school, and no new coach yet for girls' track, this story would be over, if the flame of love were not running deep. Gabe's interactions prove amazingly supportive with family, friends, and colleagues, but kept away from Candy, he never begins to realize how stigmatized she is. She spares him any angst she can because she loves him and because she naturally tries to help their relationship survive.

It's decided she must be transferred to Dorsey High to bring a final end to illegal activity and disruption of protocol. Oddly, Jefferson in this case acts against its star coach and star student, sinking instantly back into mediocrity. A sad air of insignificance follows their removal from campus, and an end to an era of fast-mounting, record-breaking track victories.

Despite Candy's moodiness, she leaves a legacy of valedictory performance, a ready and capable voice for the team, administration, and staff. Campus conversation in general returns to predictable without her outspoken, adamant contributions.

Gabe

As Gabe is clearing out his desk for the last time ever, Boys' Track Coach Johnson and Coach Chapell, both Black, are sitting at their respective desks, so close to him they could throw spitballs at each other as they had often before his removal from campus. The memory of such games and laughter seems sad now to Gabe as he "holds cool" through his last good-bye to the department.

"I don't know why you don't just deny the whole thing, man. It's her word against yours," Johnson suggests. He tries to catch Gabe's eye directly and non-stop in hopes of stirring him to action.

"Yeah, nobody can prove it," Chapell adds.

"I don't want to deny it," Gabe states, totally frustrated that this response is becoming a redundant mantra for everyone who advises him.

Johnson explodes at this naïve reply. "What? You want to go to jail? Hell, this shit happens. You're not the first. Don't get me wrong; I ain't saying it's right. It just ain't worth going to jail for. If it was me, I'd straight-out claim it never happened."

Worse images spark Chapell at the thought of jail time. "You go down for this, you'd better watch your back," he says fast and nervously. "A White dude screwing around with a young Black girl doesn't sit well with the brothers in lock-up. Hell, it doesn't sit right with a lot of brothers, period."

Gabe tries one more time to explain what no one has yet accepted. "You don't understand. It isn't just a sexual thing."

"I suppose you love the girl," Chapell says, looking sadly at the floor.

"Course he does," Johnson finishes. "But does she love him?"

"Yeah, we want to be together," Gabe answers.

Chapell gets up at this point and walks over to Gabe. "Okay then, you sap. Go to her parents and tell them about your intentions. Tell them that you love their daughter, that this isn't some sleazy affair."

"But they won't listen to me," Gabe says, stopping there, knowing there's too much to this subject for conversation.

"Yeah. Well, I guess you can't blame them. They probably want to bury your ass under the penitentiary."

"Wait! What is she, 17?" Johnson starts. "Then you don't need her parents' permission."

"Permission for what?" says Gabe."

Thinking he has the perfect solution, Johnson pounds on the desk. "To get married in Nevada! Drive to Vegas and get hitched. A wife can't be compelled to testify against her husband."

At all this, Gabe just raises his eyebrows to show both consideration and hopelessness. He thumps the back of his old friends, waves and leaves. He leaves: He leaves the office, the campus, his first significant job, the girls' team, and the many early-morning runs with Candy.

Three weeks later, Johnson calls on behalf of Neal who begs him to ask Gabe to attend the week's LA City High School Track Championship. Neal, accustomed to a pep talk from Gabe, feels he needs to see him at the meet. He's not ready to stand alone without his favorite coach. Gabe goes to the championship. Everything is comfortable and usual for him, and he and Neal make plans to stay in touch. Dawn is there, too, and she breaks the school two-mile record for Jefferson, just the way things were in the old days. She also breaks down in tears.

Mopping up her wordless face with his handkerchief, Gabe comforts her. "Dawn, don't cry. You deserve this achievement, and I know it as well as anyone who knows you."

Later the Jefferson contingent reveals their view of Dawn's day in a campus newsletter. "She won, and she's great, but she had to cry because she wanted to win for her coach, and that coach is just a fan now."

Candy

Candy, totally uninvited to nostalgic reunions of Jefferson athletes, reunites with her mom enough to settle some things.

"Ma, it was never what you thought," she shares on the porch swing with the same favorite family lemonade.

"Baby, you jus' work with me now. I want you to work with me. It was sex, and you too young, and we don't do what men want. You knew that. Everybody knows that. You're in trouble now. You have to leave this place."

"God, Mom, I'm not pregnant. It wasn't fly by night. Where do I have to go, and why?"

"You can't stay where you turned into Frankenstein, Baby. Everybody knew you as da winner. Now everybody knows you as da loser."

At this Candy leaps off the swing, crashing its backside into the wall. "I'm not a loser. I'll never be a loser. Loving someone is not being a loser. Loving Gabe . . . " Candy cannot finish.

"Whoa, girl. I'm not send'n you to Timbuktu to hide out. I've been look'n into this and your principal says he can transfer you to Dorsey in Baldwin Hills. It's far . . ."

"How far?" Candy asks.

"Around five miles, thirty minutes by bus," says her mom. "You quit those early morn'n jogs and you'll be ahead of yourself. You'll have more time to work on a scholarship than here. Those girls on your team is mean. They don't wanna work with you anymore. Their parents don't want'm hanging out with you."

"They're jealous." Candy resumes fighting stance. "Everybody loves Gabe, and I got'm, and he doesn't care about anyone but me, and they couldn't even hold a decent conversation with him or run half as far as we do together every day."

"Did," her mom rubs in. "The point is you're cooked. We have to start over. You need a fresh start and get this man outa your head. He's gone, so you might as well be gone, too. The story's over."

This part of the porch conversation is impossible for Candy. It's true everybody's on her case, not just the girls but even the teachers, and believe it or not, there is no coach, the one thing she'd needed the most since she was 15.

"I suppose they'll get us a coach someday, a lady coach," Candy drones hopelessly as she aims for her room to be alone.

These days being alone is all she can hope for. It's starting to feel relieving to be away from people who don't understand, which is everybody except Gabe. It probably is best to change schools, so she shouts a low moan of acceptance to her mom as she slumps down the hall to her room. "Okay."

That's all. She doesn't care much about details, not even to fight back for her future with Gabe, which if not sooner, she can demand at 18, only months away.

However, Dorsey proves no boost. It's a sort of trade-off of bitterness for boredom. Frankly, even sports, without Gabe as her coach, offer little interest anymore. Staying to herself becomes Candy's new style, even in the cafeteria, but she has a dream, and she knows it is real.

In this period Candy composes more songs than ever, great songs, sung well from her sultry episodes on the porch. She sings, not like the famous Blues singers her family came to LA to celebrate, but like Janis Joplin, throwing gnarling insults at an unfair world.

Ashes in the Wind

Ashes in the wind
Scattering my memories
Hidden deep within—
And my teardrops
Run slowly down my face,
Yet to be erased
Like ashes in the wind.

—Chorus *"Ashes in the Wind,"*
from Candy's Album

Gabe and Candy's Dad, Earl

The legal phrase "Anything you say or do can be held against you" begins to permeate Gabe's days now. Pandora is now beginning to unleash more heinous injustice upon Gabe than he ever dreamed of. He's the same do-gooder he always was, but aware of his stubborn choice to hold onto Candy against the better judgment of all humanity, he begins to face what that means and to feel what a lousy existence he's created. Disallowed to teach for an unknown period to be spent hashing through frustrating legalities, he has at the very least a lot to think over. He also lives in the shadow of Candy's side of the story and needs to think through how to help her and relate to each other when they're not allowed to.

After a free session with his therapist buddy, Jon, he heads back to Westwood and considers skipping his eight-mile run for the day for the first time since. . . well. . . for the first time. He stretches out on his couch and moves to turn on the TV, when it occurs to him it's time for local news, and it's entirely possible he is the local news. So he changes his mind and skips TV, realizing how many parts of ordinary life he has to skip these days.

He twists on the couch, one more discomfort to take on like Sir Lancelot in King Arthur's Court. He does feel like Lancelot, the court's greatest knight and companion, eventually besmirched by an irreverent love affair with Arthur's wife. But the story is only slightly encouraging for Gabe since there's no gallant court of manners to support him anything like what Lancelot knew. The entire system's against me, he thinks, as he turns over gently in hopes of a short nap.

But a horrid front door buzz totally crunches that hope, and hearing it throws Gabe into an immediate sit-up position with his eyes cast on the door. *I know one thing I can do while my career's on vacation*, he thinks. *I can change that buzzer to a chime.* The buzz resumes, in fact, in a way it has never buzzed before. Someone is desperate about something, and Gabe's question is whether he's desperate enough himself to face whoever it is. It could be Candy, standing right where she should not be. It could be Jon, following up with a soothing drink or something. He's paid the rent, so it's not the landlady. He moves up to the door, and in Lancelot mode, faces it. It's buzzing more than he thinks buzzers are supposed to.

"Who is it?" Gabe checks firmly, asking from inside a locked door.

But a silence sets in. The combination of no answer and no more buzzing is stupefying. It's not Candy or Jon. So he opens it to discover Earl Mills reeking of alcohol.

"Mr. Mills," "Lancelot" offers in a perfect neutral mode no one could accuse of any kind of attitude.

Earl Mills, Candy's father, is standing there, clearly a mere 10 years older than Gabe. He's raving mad and likely to bust the buzzer if Gabe closes the door in his face. He's in a rage—sweaty, seething, advancing, and finally lunging into the face of Gabe. "What did you say to my wife?" he mouths in gnarled language, charging meanly, all spit, in pit bull fashion.

"What do you mean?" Gabe asks, as he backs into the living room.

"You came to my house an' played up ta my wife," he charges.

"No way!" Gabe backs away from the alcoholic stench and clenched fist. "That's not true. I just needed to talk to her. I still do."

Earl gets into Gabe's face.

Gabe is blasted with Earl's breath. He says, "Look, I know you've been drinking. Why don't you go home and . . ."

Suddenly, Earl grabs at Gabe's throat, and the two men stumble onto the apartment floor. The view from there is of a shrine of runners' memorabilia, thirty-five running trophies in a room filled with shelves and posters, all shaking precipitously as the two rumble emotionally like two wrestlers suddenly thrown into the ring. Gabe, on a smart move to be expected of a guy who drinks iced tea, breaks free of Earl's clutches and backs up a step. In bruised and broken form, he nearly swallows the line he's wanted to say to Candy's parents all along. "I don't want to fight you, Mr. Mills. Just let me explain."

At this, Earl is on his feet, not to listen but to take another swing at Gabe, but he misses. He goes for Gabe's neck again and slams his head against a door frame. Gabe grimaces, wishing he'd never opened the door, and manages to grab Earl around the waist, and they tumble out the front door onto the lawn. Gabe pins Earl's wrists to the ground and squints from the stench of beer. He barely manages to mouth the words: "Stop, and I'll let you up!"

Earl surrenders and backs toward his car with, "You go near my daughter again—I'll shoot you!" He opens the car door and falls into the seat, his feet on the curb and his hands on both sides of his aching head. Gabe's athletic timing jumps at this silent second of triumph with the kind of comment that's been running through his dreams for months.

"Let me help you, Mr. Miills. You need some ice, a glass of water." He takes off his tee shirt, wads it up and throws it to Earl. "You need to go back to Candy and Delois, and everybody talk."

"You," Earl rants, moving over to start his car and leave. "You needa hide your face. You needa get outa my family."

Gabe watches Earl pull away, staring at him earnestly but wordlessly. He gets back in, double-locks the door, has a long painful shower, and calls Jon. He wants to call Candy, but that's not only illegal, but dangerous. On top of that, their love is being squelched by her parents. What does he say to Jon-- that he's been beaten to a pulp, that Delois misunderstood him saying, "She'd like him if she got to know him," that Earl is both confused and drunk, or just that he can't watch the local news anymore?

INTERRACE

A Celebration of the Human Race!   November/December 1989 $3.95

Gabe and
Candy
Grosz

Premier Issue!

Gabe with his children, 1993

Candy Mills

HEAR CANDY SING HER TOP SONGS

Recorded at Metro Studios LA with Tom Thomas, Music Producer, 1998. Choose Google: https://soundcloud.com/thegabigoldstein

Candy's voice, reminiscent of Janis Joplin, rails about love, womanhood, understanding, and misunderstanding. She speaks forcefully the messages of the Black Diaspora and the famous South Central Black Jazz singers of the 30's and 40's who preceded her at her neighborhood Dunbar Club long before she moved there.

Hence she lists her singer name as Billee in honor of Billie Holiday, her favorite. Though happily married to Gabe Grosz when these songs came out, she uses her professional name Billie Candace Mills here, a combination of her maiden, married, and singer names.

SONG TITLES:

Pretty in Black	Mr. Radioman
Strong Again	Monday Morning Blues
I'll Be There	No Next Time
The Next Time	Everybody Knows
Your Hero	Have You Ever?
Young lovers	Crazy for You
Cold Water	Modern Day Slave Girl
How Could You?	Out of My Head
Falling in Love	He Loves Me (He Loves Me Not)

CHAPTER FOUR

The Eye of the Storm

The next morning is raw with nothing. Gabe wakes up to a brand new day that cannot possibly be what it is—the day after an attack by Candy's father, his first day out of school without a job, a throbbing body that hurts no matter which way he turns it, and a burning desire to just talk to the girl of his dreams, which fortune similar to that of Romeo and Juliet forbids him.

But the mirror is his friend. Lunging somewhat painfully into the bathroom, he finds all bruises are in spots clothes will cover. All the blood that dripped is on the collar of a shirt easy to toss. But whose blood is it? God, who cares? Is Candy's family insane or what? It doesn't matter. He does not question Candy or themselves as a couple. He will stand up to being defamed, the way he would have stood up for any athlete on his team, any student in his class.

He swears again to play the Lancelot role and face the court sober and assured. He showers long enough to numb his wounds and heads for the police station to register his side of the case. He believes in love, not illegal sex, and he prepares to take the first step in re-identifying himself, setting Earl's assault straight with the authorities at least.

West LA Police Station, May 1981

As Gabe approaches the cop house, he carefully calculates for the first time in his life the proportion of Blacks to Whites. It does matter, he figures, noting an almost totally Anglo scenario. This is probably the best setting for treatment he can hope for. He sees the desk sergeant has his hands full trying to calm an irate pack of citizens complaining about a drug gang, so Gabe weaves his way past the clamor and approaches another officer.

Gabe faces him with his statement head-on: "I want to report an incident. I was involved in a fight last night at my home."

"Do you want to file a complaint?

"No, no. I don't want to do that. I just want it to be on record in case it happens again."

"All right. What's your name?"

"Grosz.... G-r-o-s-z. Gabriel Grosz."

At this, the officer stops to jog his memory. "Grosz . . . hm. That name sounds familiar. Have a seat."

Gabe is surprised and not at all happy to sound familiar. A few minutes later, a plain clothes detective comes out of the back and approaches with his nose in paperwork.

"I'm Detective Harper. Are you Grosz? Are you aware that a complaint has been filed against you?"

Gabe answers "No, I'm not" twice, his first answer swallowed in shock.

"Come with me," says Harper, swiftly ushering Gabe to the lonelier back of the room and on into a sterile interview room.

There's nothing there but the good cop/bad cop staging and stacks of papers sorted significantly across the tabletop. Gabe slides weakly into one of the chairs and sits nervously straight up. His posture is perfect, and his bruised face further reddened by shock. He believes he could faint. Harper and a thirtyish female detective, Utley, stand across from him. Utley opens a manila folder and places it on the table for Gabe to see.

"Mr. Grosz, this is a copy of a complaint and restraining order against you. It's been filed by a Mrs. Delois Mills. Do you know her?"

A sullen Gabe nods, "Yes."

"There's also a warrant for your arrest."

Harper then takes over, presenting the warrant. "Please read the complaint, Mr. Grosz and tell me if it's an accurate account of what transpired."

Gabe, the academic, reads the large and the fine print thoroughly and quickly to a drumming silence.

"Is this what happened to the best of your knowledge?" Harper presses Gabe with a searing stare.

Gabe breaks the silence with a wide sigh. "It is."

Utley careens to the space behind Gabe, massively covering it in her blues, belt and night stick, reaching around from behind him from both sides.

"Mr. Grosz, you're under arrest for statutory rape. You have a right to remain silent. Anything you do or say may be used against you in a court of law. You have the right to an attorney. If you cannot afford one, one will be provided by the court."

She takes him by the arm and stands him in front of a camera. A bright light flashes out from one side. He's turned to the left, and it flashes again.

"Do you understand your rights as I have just stated them? Mr. Grosz, you are charged with violation of Penal Code Section 261.5C.—Unlawful sexual intercourse."

At this, Gabe hears a thick metal door slamming him into a cell. The sound is not real but a slam against himself inside Gabe's head. There is no unusual sound to the closing of the door to the cell they immediately place him in. It is just the idea of finding himself in any cell, anywhere, ever.

Gabe looks up, looks around. He sees a urinal and a bench, a bench too small to accommodate the four male suspects encased there. He sees the suspects are real people, taking turns on the bench, standing away from the toilet, and asking what anyone would ask anyone under the circumstances:

"What-ja in for?" "How long you been here?" and "Is this your first time?"

Of course, no one's making anyone feel better, especially Gabe. One tall, gangly Black fellow with cool athletic shoes and thick, black-rimmed glasses prefers to slowly pace the cell. He finally stops face to face with Gabe and announces the way he sees it.

"Look man, I know how it is, but a White man with a young Black girl? Lord, that's not gonna sit well with the brothas anywhere, especially not on the inside."

The word guilty begins to upset Gabe's stomach. He knows guilt is the issue and he doesn't have to admit the affair, that is, admit guilt. He could lie. He could also fudge slightly on Candy's consent and lay blame on her as a seductress. A public vote at Jefferson would be overwhelmingly in his favor. He could ask her to lie about him, for him. But she's not the one in danger of going to jail and ruining her future.

He knows what his choices are, but he is a born Lancelot, a born truth-teller, everyone's gallant friend and strongest back-up, a romantic with his heart on his sleeve. If in love with the king's wife, he will admit it, sweep her up upon his white horse, and ride triumphantly off into a blood-red sunset for those who tell the truth and live the truth in agonizing valor.

Officer Utley explains to him politely that placing him temporarily in a holding cell is required because he has admitted guilt, and he stays wobbly but tight-mouthed in the face of these pronouncements.

"We're going to let you go," Utley explains, "but you have to come back tomorrow. You must come back and turn yourself in. You face the judge tomorrow."

Before leaving the precinct, Gabe asks around, closing the experience with the same focus he started with, wondering what the racial composition is tomorrow. He finds out that his arraignment judge will be a Black female.

The day after Gabe's arrest, he returns to the courtroom attached to the police station. He goes bright and early, almost as if he'd never left. He goes alone as if just going to the library to return a book or perform an everyday task. He asks himself what more he should do, but he can't think of anything. They do not suggest a lawyer, and Jon is busy at work. He is sure there's no more to the criminal heresy than answering perfunctory questions.

He enters the larger room near the holding space he'd been in the night before. It doesn't look like his idea of a courtroom, without the high ceilings and massive wooden doors we know from TV dramas. It's full but not crowded, and the judge's voice is not particularly loud or fierce. There's a hum in the room, but it's at a respectful level. After taking a seat, he finds that people's eyes are speaking more than their mouths. It's easy to tell which ones are going before the judge. They're checking out everything, listening hard to those with them, and they sit up straight as if all the accused are immediately asked to rise to the judge's desk now.

Quicker than expected, the PA system calls out, "Mr. Grosz, Mr. Gabriel Grosz!"

Gabe approaches the bench, nodding to the public defender, who is suddenly by his side, but proceeds as if there is no defense for his side. Gabe does not quite know about such things as options like marrying in another state or obtaining a statement of consensual conduct from Candy. He doesn't know he might need a lawyer.

The Black female, a fortyish judge, reads the charge before her, repeating "unlawful sexual intercourse."

"How do you plead?" she asks to a deafening courtroom.

Gabe does not answer.

"I need your plea, Mr. Grosz." But he does not know how to answer, and the otherwise hectic courtroom stops to hear his reply.

He turns to the public defender and whispers, "I don't want to deny anything. I want to plead guilty." The public defender quickly turns to Gabe and says, "No, no! Under no circumstance should you plead guilty."

At this, the ringing voice of the female judge breaks in with, "I don't have all day, counselor."

Suddenly and rather frighteningly, Gabe now thinks he may need a lawyer. He looks at the judge and spews out quickly a statement he never expected to utter: "I'm sorry, your honor. I plead not guilty." This is clearly done upon last-minute advice from the public defender.

He remains shocked at what he has just said, while the non-threatening judge reads out her statement, looking at Gabe with pathos in her eyes but resolution in her voice:

"Mr. Grosz, I have read the complaint filed against you, and I feel that there is sufficient cause to move for a preliminary hearing, which I'm going to set for May 21st. Because of the circumstances surrounding this case, bail will be set aside. You'll be released on your own recognizance. And in the interim, a restraining order will remain in effect. Do not—I repeat—do not have any contact with the young lady or her parents."

In quick closure, the public defender stands in civil attendance and thanks the judge. Seeing clearly that Gabe is dazed, he silently escorts him from the courtroom. Gabe's thankful to the judge and the defender. It could've been much worse. The defender, on immediate recall to the courtroom, leaves Gabe alone in the shiny corridor to counsel himself.

"God, I need a lawyer," Gabe says aloud to the first person he sees.

"Yes," the old woman assures him. "We all do."

In retrospect, Gabe knows he is a babe in the woods. How to be well-defended when he didn't even do anything is beyond him. It's a strange feeling to have a lawyer and even stranger, as he wakes up to his third day as a potential felon, to realize he doesn't even have the lawyer he was offered in the courtroom yesterday.

His phone starts ringing, and he reaches to answer it, but tops. It's going to be another day of calls from his mom, his sister, three friends and two neighbors. He's so used to saying, "Don't worry; we're in love," that he decides to skip answering until he thinks of what to say now, now that yesterday's ten-minute-free-counsel got him to plead not guilty. At least one person understands this story . . . not just he and Candy. Why can't he mention the one thing he feels best about doing in his whole life?

The tendency to flip the TV on also continues to feel wrong. With all the murders in LA, who would care to publicize my case on TV? With no real pause, he immediately answers that one for himself. Some local Westside reporter; that's who. Hmm. Gabe even eats breakfast faster than ever, as if he has a full day of defense moves ahead of him. In reality,,

he has none, no idea what to do next, except submit to a lawyer as fast as he can get one.

It's so unfair that he can't discuss this with Candy! Somehow talking to her makes him into an aggressor. But the case is not about him; it's about them. They have a relationship, and now is when they need each other. But somehow, the ass-backward legal system prevents everything human, on top of accusing rape!

At the start of the next day, with all its impossible questions, he's already exhausted at 8:35 am, skips breakfast and temporarily unplugs his phone. He looks at himself in the bathroom mirror with all the bright lights on and records progress on healing the scars from Candy's father's attack. But he finds himself not recognizable to himself. He stares awhile wondering what a rapist looks like and if he might look like one to anyone. He wonders if he'd scare a few of the more mindless students if he showed up at school. For a few seconds, applying imagination to his scarred-up face, he scares himself.

Gabe's sister, Lily, his lifetime supporter, calls from her busy work to share the name of a criminal lawyer suggested by her best friend's brother.

She tells him, "This guy's cool, Gabe. He's young and assertive."

"Okay," says Gabe. "I have no idea how to evaluate these guys." He's immediately off to his car and the legal neighborhood.

The road to Century City is paved with gold is the sarcastic thought that runs through his head as he directs himself fifteen minutes southeast to a business district of fashionable high rises that seem to sneer down on his Westwood neighborhood, as if to say, "You're a little short in more ways than one." The thought causes Gabe to glide into underground parking for Howard Curtz,—Criminal Attorney, take the first space, park, open his wallet and give some thought to how much cash he's carrying and how much money he's worth (or not) overall.

He'd leave on a dime if he had a single excuse. Instead he stops first to take in the posh setting of a parking garage that looks like a hotel lobby, complete with a doorman for the elevator and a preponderance of valet parking attendants. He fears he may not have enough for parking and tips to reach this lawyer, much less what it'll cost to swing his case.

The glass-walled elevator makes absolutely no sound as it glides to the top floor, looking out on an entire block of towering palm trees set in green-green grass with tall lilies in various shades. When it stops as motionlessly as it climbed, the door opens to a pretty secretary with her hand outstretched to Gabe.

"Mr. Grosz? Mr. Curtz is waiting for you right now. Come with me."

Gabe does not mind an escort at this minute and greets her somewhat thankfully, tromping awkwardly through large rooms of overly thick carpeting.

Oh, it's Curtz! He's a bit undersized for the long desk where he seems to reside amid files, paper stacks, ash trays with ashes and butts, two brass lamps, and a coffee carafe!

"Can I get you something?" the secretary continues.

"No, not really," answers Gabe, eager to figure anything out about the danger he's in and how much it's going to cost.

"Have a seat, Mr. Grosz," Curtz starts.

Gabe hears a slow, heavy drumbeat in his head, swallows, and lets their four caustic eyes engage. They start, each feeling the other out, unsure of enough trust for real collaboration. An image flashes through Gabe's mind of a dream lawyer, a robust minority type, overweight, warmly shaking hands with him with a smile and the projection—"This case is a piece of cake, Gabe. Let's record a few details and go grab a beer!"

Instead, his dapper counsel is overdressed and overworked, keeping his eye on the buttons on his phone that keep changing colors, twinkling and buzzing, a guy with eyes looking over you and not into you. Oh well. Gabe just hopes Lily knows what she's doing with this recommendation.

Curtz leans forward in his enormous soft leather desk recliner. He's thirtyish, White, and a bit distant about the whole dramatic malaise.

"Here it says, 'California Penal Code —Sec. 261-5C.' That's statutory rape, Mr. Grosz."

He then leans comfortably way back and strokes his colorful silk tie in silent thought.

"How do you like this tie, Mr. G.? I had the best decorator money can buy set up this place. When I moved in, she gave me this tie as a gesture of appreciation. The little things are comforting in a case like this. Rape!"

Feeling more accused than rescued, Gabe glances around the room by the best decorator money can buy.

"Well . . ." he replies and halts, looking for support.

"As I understand it now, you've been charged," Curtz continues.

Gabe almost says, "Yes, sir" at this point, until he reconsiders that he may be the only real sir in the room. "That's right," Gabe admits.

"Well," Curtz offers, opening up and serving liberally a small pinkish box of Sherman's tiny, brown-wrapped Turkish cigarettes. " Do you smoke these singularly fragrant babies, Gabriel?" He stops to stretch out his long legs as if doing yoga. Then he plunks down his key point. "You know, this case could land you four years in prison?"

To this, Gabe offers, "I don't smoke" and a blank look of disillusion to the nightmare posed as a question.

"So you pleaded not guilty?"

"That's right."

"You know, if she doesn't testify, there's no case. But if she does take the stand, and you get a felony conviction, it'll be four years."

"Four years? Doesn't it matter that I love her?"

"Unfortunately, love doesn't fix this one. Um. . . what's her mother like?"

"She doesn't want me seeing her."

"And her father?"

"He feels the same."

Curtz squirms on his throne and rubs his face pensively. Gabe asks him what he's thinking, and Counsel drawls out his inner thought: "It's about something I read about fathers of young girls who seek out older men. It probably has no bearing." He clears his throat. "All right. Let's move on. What's your status with the school board?"

"I've been suspended without pay until the outcome of the case."

"It's going to be a challenge, but I will represent you. You don't have any priors, so if things go our way, I may be able to get you off with probation. But by all means, don't make it harder on me and you. Avoid any communication and contact with the girl."

"I can do that," Gabe answers with hidden doubt, wondering why this cigarillos fan is so wrapped up in his smoking at a time like this. He asks Curtz, "Is there something else? You look lost in an idea or something?"

"Um-hmm." Curtz perks forth, sitting up straight and tall for the first time. "I never tried a case like this. I have a lawyer friend in San Francisco. I'm going to call him for suggestions."

He sinks back down into his cushy lounger and gestures to Melissa to hand Mr. Grosz an envelope because the session is over. Gabe opens it on the spot and pulls the numbers out of three pages of legalese—$2,000 due immediately for case retention, $1,000 today and the rest before the final judgement.

The lawyer's parting words, complete with his handshake and Melissa's assistance to the door, are "There'll be other bills, but we can take them as they come."

Gabe would've cried on the elevator if he'd been a kid. Instead, he starts into a numb state with the first thought being that he doesn't feel like talking to anyone right now, especially Lily. He's thinking to unplug the phone again for the second time today. Lastly, he wishes even harder than before that he could talk to Candy about their situation. When he gets home, it happens. The phone rings the minute he's in, and there's a heavy, almost anguished wish that it would be Candy. And it is. My God, it is!

"Gabe, Gabe! I love you. I'm going to call you tonight, when everyone's asleep. I have to go now. No chance. Bye, love."

Gabe manages to say only, "Candy?"

When she hangs up with one more "bye," she says it both slowly and quickly, hesitating, then hanging up fast.

God! Nobody can talk to anybody! Candy can't talk to him. He isn't ready to talk to Lily. Curtz's talking to someone else because he never had a Section 261-5C case! Somehow Gabe knows at least the judge really will have something to say to him that he's standing there right now wanting to know.

Waiting for Candy's illegal call eventually makes Gabe's day. He admits criminal intent on this and laughs at himself. *If how I live is so criminal, waiting to hear from my girlfriend, I'm back to wanting to plead guilty. I must be a real criminal because I not only want to talk to her, but I don't even feel guilty about it.*

He runs his standard LA Country Club miles on the edge of the Wilshire corridor, and is glad he hasn't called Jon to join him. Too much is happening. His head does not feel sufficiently prepped for any of it, reporting to family and friends, dealing with Curtz, costs, or facing the Superior Court Hearing in two days.

Candy, even less secure than Gabe, experiences no pleasure in ruminating over their challenges and confusion. She walks out of the hell of 4309 Lima Street into a cold, dark, and rainy night, feeling some of the kind of relief known to Iranians who flagellate themselves in the streets. It should feel worse, but it feels better. What she asks penance for is allowing her parents to abuse her because she fell in love with an older man, the best man she's ever met or ever will meet. They owe her something for her top grades, top track times, and her painful love of them when they are their least lovable.

Why don't they trust me? I'm always right. I have to lead everybody, myself, my parents, the class, the team; hell, I'm gonna lead Gabe and move this case along. I'll write a Blues song about it, and in a few months, we'll all sit down and laugh together and have a champagne toast, because I'll be eighteen.

She thinks all this boldly, but with tears in her eyes, holding a large grocery bag, beginning to soak with water, that holds nothing but her night clothes and her favorite book, *Walden*, by Henry David Thoreau.

Candy takes shelter in a phone booth from which she can now see the torrents building up and slashing against her but can stay mostly dry instead of getting drenched. She dials Gabe, who is sound asleep in bed.

Blindly, he fumbles for the receiver and puts it to his ear. Drowsily, a frog in his throat, he says, "Hello . . . Candy?"

"Come pick me up, Grosz. I'm leaving home. I'm at the corner of Central and 41st. I can't go back now."

Gabe snaps wide awake and sits up. "Are you sure you want to do this? Of course, I want to be with you, but . . ."

"If you don't take me, where else am I going to go? I don't want to go back home. I've thought long and hard about this, and I know what I'm doing. I want to be with you. Please come pick me up, Grosz. I'm scared here all by myself."

Adrenaline turns Gabe into a male machine. "All right. We probably shouldn't be doing this . . . Okay. I'll be there as soon as I can."

The blood of Lancelot is pouring through his veins. Without a white horse, he sprints to his car and is off to South Central in the middle of the night. She holes up inside the folding glass doors of the rain-slashed phone booth, until he arrives.

Then Lancelot pulls up, spies her, opens the booth and holds her, his sopping backside in the rain. He feels her, shaking from everything at hand, not warm the way a body should be, begin to, as we say—melt into his arms.

"We're okay, Grosz. . . I know it," she breathes into his ear.

After twenty, silent, cuddled-together moments in Gabe's car, they take off for Westwood and run like scared mice through the freezing night into his apartment.

It's a dream night, though illegal, for them. Together, they are not tense. They glug hot tea after shedding wet clothes and review Gabe's trophies and awards, all polished and gleaming, set in various lighted shelves in his reliably tidy and homey man cave. Candy wears her summer pj's, and she grabs Thoreau.

"Grosz, I feel fine now. I'm so much better with you. All I want is to read you the Thoreau passage I read every night when you're not there. Okay. Just flake out now and listen to this." She fluffs up the pillows behind Gabe first and dabs a few old raindrops off his forehead with a sheet. She clears her throat. "Okay. Are you ready? 'Go confidently in the direction of your dreams. Live the life you have imagined. It's not what you look at that matters. It's what you see.'"

This, like a bedtime story for a toddler, puts Gabe into a silly trance. He sinks further into the sloppy bed and smirks. Candy turns on the TV, more than satisfied with *Happy Days* and *The Fonz*.

Gabe meanders through his relaxed brain. "Well, who looks better, Henry David or the Fonz?"

"Are you kidding? Thoreau had a beard. It's in. That is, it's in now . . . and it was. You take the Fonz. I'll take Thoreau."

"Does that mean I have to grow a beard?" Gabe mumbles half asleep.

"Not you. You already have enough hair."

In all their dog-eat-dog days, this is their happiest moment. They live momentarily off the fat of the land.

"We're in God's country, here together," murmurs Gabe almost in a twilight state.

"I saved a cornbread muffin from the cafeteria this morning," she tells him, stuffing a morsel in his mouth. "You'd better wash it down with your tea and go to sleep."

Candy turns off the TV and the lights and takes in the exquisite outdoor view of green wet tree leaves shining in the streetlights and Gabe stretched out sweetly with his eyes closed.

But tomorrow starts in frightening ambivalence. Our lovers are together under the wire and against the law. Shakespeare says of Juliette and Romeo, "The sun for sorrow will not show his head." And so, the two rise at the first sign of light into a day of gray aura, covering a dewy, still damp world. Candy is instantly in her yesterday clothes and Gabe pulls on his runner's stuff as if it were a second skin he was born in. They eat granola bars, warm their throats with hot chocolate, and run back to the car as fast as they left it last night.

"Does today scare you?" Candy asks him as they pull out of the Wilshire Corridor toward the hills of Brentwood, their favorite run.

"You know more than I do. Should I be?" Gabe replies. His eyes are huge, wide open, and frankly, scared.

"Well, yeah. We have to be. We're in the cauldron now, the witches brew. God knows what they're souping up against us. As soon as we finish running, I want to go to Curtz with you. Tomorrow, we'll be in court. I want to puff''m up. He doesn't expect to meet me, right?"

"No way. But you're right. We should cut this short," says Gabe. "We're on the run. Gee we are, we were, we're supposed to be running. But this is too Bonnie and Clyde. I hope nobody knows where we are. I don't even want to see your father in court. Talk about violence."

In the hills above Sunset Boulevard, past and behind Mount St. Mary's College, they bathe their pro-runner's bodies in a beautiful muscle-rhythm run. Such runners simply running is as grand as anything Mother Nature ever bestowed on gazelles or theater has ever seen in ballet. Nothing is going wrong in this stolen moment for them, and their veins pulsate perfectly, their breath courses divinely. They don't need Westwood or South Central, or Candy's family's house or Gabe's apartment. All they need is a pup tent on the soft earth trail with a copy of anything in it by Thoreau.

They need to be together, and they need a place to hide. Two weeks hence, Gabe will lose his apartment anyway for lack of a salary to pay for it. But the peace right now of the foot falls thudding, the wet leaves smushing, the loving breeze embracing is enough for them before they face Candy's parents in court. The attack dogs that are already sworn in for a fight.

Next, the two are off to Curtz's law office.

"Candy, I hate to take you there. I don't know where this thing with Curtz is going. I can't afford him, and he has no background in statutory. . . I'm not going to say rape. He has no background in statutory sex."

"Can I meet him, though? I want him, all of us, to know where I am. Here. I'm right here for you. The hearing's tomorrow. You have to see him anyway."

"Right, but I was thinking of getting out of it by just calling and seeing if he has any point for us today. He charges a fortune every time I go. It might work as well to just phone."

Gabe dials his phone to find out that good old Money Man seriously recommends he meet Candy today, especially since they're together at the moment already. In Century City, up the famous elevator, the two are seated with ginger ales and there are no Turkish cigarettes in sight this time. Curtz calls Candy "Candace," and is cordial.

"I wish I were meeting you under better circumstances," he bows, a tall man condescending to a short woman. "But what are you two thinking? Being together right now isn't the best thing for either of you. Now, I can't tell you what to do, Miss Mills, however, talking to you on a professional level—you being a minor—I advise you to go back home."

"I'm not going back." Candy is nothing if not direct. She says this looking first at Curtz, then at Gabe, and reaching for Gabe's hands for support. Gabe looks back at her and holds her hands in acquiescence. He does not fully know what he is learning from her at the moment.

"Well, okay," says Curtz.

What can he say? At the moment, almost no one represents Candy's best interests at all.

"As you know, Gabriel, your preliminary hearing is tomorrow. Candace, if you choose not to appear in court, the case against Mr. Grosz can possibly be dismissed."

"Mr. Curtz," Candy adds. "I'm not the one who brought charges against Gabe. I don't want to testify against him, and I want you to know that. This is one of the reasons I left home."

"I see. I don't know what the two of you are going to do from here on. But Gabriel, in addition to the statutory rape charge, you are now harboring a minor. Her parents may be looking for her, and if I were them, one of the places I would look is your apartment."

"My parents don't know I've had contact with Gabe since he's been dismissed from school," says Candy.

"I see," Curtz murmurs, his brain screaming for these two to employ even a little bit of common and legal sense. "So, what are your plans?" he asks her.

"We're going to get married in Las Vegas."

This reply is even quite specific news for Gabe, and subtly appears to raise a skeptical vein in the lawyer, who nonetheless says nothing more.

"Okay then, you two. First we have to see to the case. Nine o'clock sharp!" He stands and bows again, shaking their hands and settling back in his over-sized, cushioned chair to stare out his wall of windows overlooking the cruel city below.

On the way out, Gabe hears Curtz barely from across the room. The lawyer is rudely aghast and talking aloud to himself . . . "Jesus, Las Vegas?"

Today is not yesterday. It is so different from any day these two have ever endured. It is its own tomorrow and a hint and wish for tomorrows ahead. But for the moment, Curtz, Candy, and Gabe, are focused on the more important tomorrow—the very next day in court—when the four will align and fight with words to define what the real tomorrows will be for all of them.

Later, back at Gabe's, after lentil soup, cheese sandwiches and apple juice, a barefoot Candy hurdles his sunken couch and sprawls out there. The two cuddle together for thirty minutes of Cronkite.

"I won't make national news. This is okay," he announces with amazing calm. "Don't turn on anything local, though, all right?"

"It's out there, Grosz. You're not paranoid. Some day when we're old and gray I'll tell you what they said."

True or not, this is a joke for them, and they laugh a little, wrinkling faces at each other. Their more nervous moments stay silent. But . . . CRASH! The sound Candy fears to hear breaks their momentary comfort. They freeze and hold back even their breathing.

Candy leaps to the TV, closing it out as she lands on it. She stands with her back to it, terrified. "It's my parents!"

Gabe jumps up next to her, freezes too, then barely whispers in her left ear, "How do you know?"

She does not answer, only staring back at his whisper in motionless amazement. Crashing continues. It's glass breaking in the panels of the front door. The two exquisite athletes, like Ninjas, first strike their ready pose, then, leaving no sound of breathing or a single footfall, move out of the room. Gabe lunges toward the door, but so does Candy.

"You get out the back," he says.

"No, you," Candy insists, pushing him toward the safer-seeming bedroom.

But Candy's mom shrieks out to them, "Open this goddam door, Mr. Grosz! Candy, open this door! I know you're in there."

Candy follows Gabe back toward the bedroom, while breaking glass hits the floor. They hear shattering sounds, ending in the horrid crunching of broken glass of Delois and Earl making their way in, like a swat team ready to take the place down.

"You've got to get out. They're going to kill you, Grosz. Come on. Get out. Go!"

"I can't leave you here by yourself," Gabe holds, always thinking with Arthurian grace. "Let's go out the back."

"No. I can't. You—you go! Go! They won't kill me."

Candy is desperate for him but starting to give in for herself. She forcefully pushes him, so he hurries down the hallway, heading to the back door, where she ducks into a closet. They hear more crunching of broken glass and even more shards dropping and crashing.

Earl smoothly unlatches the front door, reaching through the smashed panels. Outside street light streams into the room where our runners have turned off the lights in their attempt to escape. The parents, slowed down by darkness and sharp shards, enter cautiously, popping shattered glass with every step.

Delois, small and sloppy, but powerful like Napoleon, announces her ultimatum: "Where are you, Grosz? Where's my daughter?

But Earl bumps into a side table, knocking it over, causing her to move back into the lighted bedroom.

"Bootsie, in here." She shoves her findings into his face: the pajamas, running shoes, the large, gold-flanked copy of Thoreau, and a large grocery bag full of books.

"That bastard," he curses. "Ain't no way she carried all this on the bus. Where are they? Maybe they took off while you were yelling."

"Call the police, Bootsie," Delois says, shoving the bedside phone into his hand. "I'm going to get a gun and blow off his fuckin' head!"

But she storms out to the living room with such drama that Earl follows, leaving the phone disconnected, with the receiver off the cradle. The parent thugs take over the living room as the new central headquarters. They're mid-combat, having merely terrorized their daughter and the man she wants to marry, and ready for round two of attack. Delois takes a pack of cigarettes out of her pocket, and like a company lieutenant taking a battle break in the trenches, falls into Gabe's couch and lights up. Earl, probably to avoid proximity to her himself, paces the room in rambling pronouncements.

This is not what the Mills are used to doing on weekends. They perform nearly humorously, except that they've already fairly destroyed Gabe's career and reversed Candy's leadership role, unchallenged track stats, and brilliant future, painting both the lovers' lives with insult and disgrace.

Just how violently they are capable of exerting their fears and revenge only Romeo and Juliet could attest to. Struggling parents who feel they are losing their promising daddy's girl to what can only be debauchery are profoundly more dangerous than standard criminals. If there were no criminals, domestic crime alone would confound the police. So Earl and Delois strategize in the dark living room, where furniture is upended and glass lies in sparkling chunks all across the floor of the room, all lighted by little more than Delois' cigarette. Meanwhile, Candy and Gabe each try to save the other, sweating in whispers outside the back door of the apartment.

Earl continues pacing with announcements. "That crazy man's got'r. . . hiding her someplace."

Delois spits out "If you were a real Black man, none of this would've ever happened. You should've killed him the first time you came here."

Their strategies deteriorate to pure bitterness, when fate would prefer they simply cry pools of crocodile tears and beg Candy and Gabe to explain and repair everyone's lives. Instead, Earl defends, not his family, but himself.

"You sayin' I'm not a man? Some men slap women like you down, woman."

"I'm the only one does any slappin' in this family," Delois states, still in lieutenant mode. "Where's the police at? I told you to call'm."

But it's not yet the police who enter. It's Gabe. Turning himself in suddenly, he approaches Earl alone, ever conciliatory, hoping a frontal word battle will give Candy on the back porch a chance to find herself a safer haven somewhere down the street. Gabe enters cautiously; but is immediately clipped by Earl, ready and raving. Earl pounces and slams Gabe again against the wall, as he did previously, and he holds him there. Gabe does not struggle. The "lieutenant" interrogates:

"Where's our daughter? Kill'm, Bootsie."

"I don't know," says Gabe, bruised badly and glad he doesn't know where Candy is.

"Goddam liar. I told ya to kill'm, Bootsie."

Earl, not really a killer and interpreting his bull of a wife to mean "hurt that dude," bangs Gabe's head, shattering a glass-covered picture. Unbeknown to Gabe, a large shard of broken glass sticks deeply into his left tricep.

"Where's Candy, goddamit? I swear I'll kill you if you've done something to her," spouts Earl.

At this Candy rushes in, shaken and torn among them. Should she save herself, Gabe, or just calm her parents down? As ever, she knows she is the crux of the affair and has all the power at hand. But her many selves back off into silent helplessness.

"Here I am," is all she says, and these remain her last words to her unchosen old family or chosen new family until she sits in the courtroom the next day.

But tonight, the night before the preliminary hearing, the police burst into this deadly apartment scene, hands on their guns. Candy speaks to them alone, though with great difficulty, because her mother answers every question asked of Candy herself.

It is as if, insulting her mother, she has become the enemy of South Central—Former Athletic Hero Turned Famous Slut—forever, to be embedded in the history of the team, the school, the neighborhood, and the family. It is as if she has no future, when she'd been promised the greatest future of anyone at Jefferson High. It is as if Gabe, who always looks like Jesus and acts like an apostle now upon the cross, standing pinned by glass to the wall of Golgotha. Against all intuition and feeling, she stands looking at this, unable even to free him or shout out loud.

At the sight of his daughter, Earl loses concentration, and Gabe releases himself, while Delois grabs Candy. She says, "Where have you been? How the hell did you get here? You better talk, girl."

But Candy does not say a word. The two White, armed, Westwood cops interrupt the horrid reunion. "We got a complaint about a domestic disturbance. Is this your apartment?" They look at their paperwork and one adds, "Mr. Grosz?"

Gabe steps outside with the cop, while the other moves swiftly over to Candy, who is trembling with fright and out of character. He motions for her to come over to him, where he is checking out the broken glass and Gabe's blood on the wall and carpet.

Delois tries to hold her war front, but this is Napoleon's Waterloo. "Don't you dare move from that spot," she says to Candy, defying the order of the law. "Have you arrested that White man yet?" she degrades the White cop who annoys her so much in this all-White neighborhood where she has just found her daughter hiding.

"He's being questioned, Ma'am."

"What do you mean 'being questioned'? What do you have to question him about? He kidnapped our 17-year-old daughter."

At this, the officer moves to separate the parents from the daughter, and with his back to her parents, he gently asks Candy, "Is that true? Have you been taken against your will?"

But Candy, stupefied by the entire scene, does not answer, unfortunately opening a chance for Delois to rant and incriminate even more.

"Yes, it's true. He's already been charged with rape, and he was ordered to stay away from her."

But the officer calmly and appropriately asks, "How do you know he took her?"

"Look in the bedroom. He's the one brought her here all right."

The officer then asks Candy in the most direct way, "The man outside with my partner. . . is he your boyfriend?"

But Candy, unable to lift any momentum, is smothered by her parents.

"He ain't her boyfriend," says Delois.

"He's her coach. He kidnapped her, goddammit!" says Earl, trying to avoid all the areas of damage in the room, and trying to get beyond the officer and over to Candy.

"Sir," the cop says, handling this domestic violence perfectly, "I need you to lower your voice."

He turns to Candy and quietly asks her, "Is that true?"

But it's Delois again who responds. "Of course, it's true."

"Excuse me, Ma'am. I'm talking to your daughter. I need both of you to let her answer."

He turns to Candy supportively, starting an opportunity for her to answer, at least for the moment, safely. "What's your name, Miss?"

"Candy Mills."

"Did your coach bring you here, Candy?"

Looking at her mother, but distanced by the broad-shouldered cop, she makes the all-time, significant statement. . . at least for the evening: "I called Mr. Grosz from a pay-phone near my house and asked him to pick me up."

"And you weren't brought here against your will?"

To this, Candy fearfully shakes her head, "No."

Her father breaks in with, "That cracker attacked me. You gonna do something about that?"

Delois adds the final insult of the night, which beautifully prepares all for tomorrow, the court case at West LA Municipal Court in the morning: "Police ain't gonna do nothing to a white man in a white neighborhood."

All the bodies shift at this point. No further charges are filed against Gabe or the Mills. Gabe and Candy barely get a chance to exchange a glance. She is not ushered home but pushed toward the door and into the Mills' car. Despite this depraved attack on Gabe, even worse looms for tomorrow's attack in court. Gabe falls awkwardly into the nearest chair, finding his apartment raped and Candy absent again, truly kidnapped now, his arm and chest wounded and aching for the second time this week. Which part hurts most is so hard to tell that Shakespeare himself might prefer to phrase it: "Romeo, come forth. Come forth thou fearful man. Affliction is enamored of thy parts, and thou art wedded to calamity."

Preliminary Hearing—West LA Municipal Court, May 21, 1981

A supportive Greek chorus moans in the background of Gabe's life, while sage, stoic healing voices rise from inside himself. But Candy's mental setting is the opposite. She has been abducted and silenced. Her parents put Pandora back into her box and lock her into it. Breaking her cannot be done, of course, but it feels like it. She has already assured Curtz that she is the case to free Gabe in court. But after her abduction, she is forced to be and feel merely 17 and powerless again, a poor Black girl born into the start but not the heart of women's lib. The runner/singer halted and silenced is the same as Juliet hidden and drugged. She is taken defeated away from Gabe, and she enters the courtroom in the morning not herself. She is withdrawn and non-committal in her parents' hands, and she abides in her Pandora's box just like Juliet, comatose in spirit, maybe worse. The Mills approach the precinct as if to attend a hanging at their request.

Candy and her parents enter smugly, Earl and DeLois wearing tight mouths and faces. Candy drags along in a posture of defeat, as if dead to the scene in which both sides expect her to play the lead.

The courtroom is the opposite, a noisy, bustling, huge assembly of echoing coughs and nervous talk. Next to Gabe, Curtz, and the Mills, sit six radical members of The Nation of Islam (Black Muslims), finishing their case. They are dressed in their signature black suits and ties. They seem interested in Gabe's situation, after legal particulars have been announced publicly for court reporters, and they move their transcriber closer to the front. Candy, looking down the whole time since she entered, notices them too. They are the only ones in shiny, black patent shoes. She is not only smothered by her parents' boiling rage but frightened at being witnessed by six members of a Black supremacy movement. Their presence seems to intimidate everyone.

Gabe is also aware of the Black Muslim group because he came earlier than the Mills, and he knows they just completed a murder case and are an uncomfortable party to be positioned next to on the docket. It seems customary to leave after your hearing is complete, but the Muslims don't. Their businesslike, black-suited outfits in no way hide from Gabe a certain dangerous aspect in their eyes, their whispers, and their impolite choice to hover over Gabe's hearing intrusively. Candy feels Blacker and Gabe Whiter as these racists stare.

Despite these and/or anyone's concerns, the melee is immediately jump-started. The judge's gavel starts pounding sharply, and those seated for later scheduled hearing halt their voices on a dime, as the judge calls for Gabe's case: "Mr. Grosz, you are charged with Penal Code 261-5C, Illegal Sexual Intercourse."

The Mills sit near the front, and Gabe sits behind Curtz at the defendant's table. At a corresponding table sits the prosecutor, a White District Attorney in her 30's. The gavel strikes again, and Candy takes the stand.

The Following Is Transcribed:

District Attorney: "Candy, tell the court what happened on April 12, 1981. And start from the beginning."

Candy: (She speaks uncomfortably, holding her collar slightly closed with her right hand, as if she feels improperly dressed.) "He, he picked me up."

D.A.: "Who picked you up, Candy?"

Candy: "Mr. Grosz picked me up."

D.A.: "I need you to speak up, Candy."

Candy: (She leans forward into the microphone, and taking note of her effect, releases her right hand from holding onto her collar.) "Mr. Grosz picked me up."

D.A.: "And then what happened?"

Candy: "We drove to a mountain trail above Bel Air." (At this, Candy looks for the first time into the D.A.'s eyes, which suggest suspicion about the trail being intentionally remote. She quickly then corrects her brevity.) "Oh, that's the one we always run because it's long and steep. We're runners."

D.A.: "What time did Mr. Grosz pick you up?"

Candy: "Around seven o'clock in the morning."

D.A.: "Did you run?"

Candy: "No. We changed our mind."

D.A.: "Did you change your minds for any particular reason?"

Candy: "I just didn't feel like running. It was raining, and I was tired."

D.A.: "What did you and Mr. Grosz do instead?"

Curtz: "Objection. It hasn't been established that these two did anything."

Judge: "Sustained."

D.A.: "I'll rephrase. You said it was raining and you were tired. What did you do?"

Candy: "We went to his apartment."

D.A.: "And what did you do there?"

Candy: "We talked, we ate, we watched some TV."

D.A.: "Did you and Mr. Grosz have sex?"

Candy: (At the conclusion of the word "sex," Candy pauses, and there is a quiet rustling of whispers across the court-room. She not only registers for the crowd as deeply Black and Gabe pale and White, but he is a mature man and she is a young girl. Luckily, the D.A. is not likely to question Gabe's role as her instructor.) "Uh, sex?"

The room is tense, the Mills iron-willed enough to all but rise from their seats with their hands in fists; Delois ready to, as usual, answer for her daughter, better than her daughter, full of truth and fire.

D.A.: "Yes. At some point on April 12, 1981, did you and Mr. Grosz have a sexual encounter in his apartment?"

The listening part all by itself has depleted Candy's emotional energy. She stops, against all protocol, as if she doesn't remember or is not allowed to address the topic. She looks at Gabe, as if he can answer for her, and quickly across the front of the room, her eyes slipping nervously past the Black Muslim bigots she knows want to "hang her" by all accounts, despite living in a country which does not do such things. Then she affirms the judge with her best reshuffling of nerve, thankful for a Black female judge, who seems, upon the second, to be a possible peer.

Judge: "Please answer the question. Yes or no?"

Candy: "Yes."

D.A.: "Was the sex your idea or was it his idea?"

Candy: "It was mutual. We planned to be together that day."

D.A.: "Which one of you initiated it?"

Candy: "We kind of did at the same time. We both wanted to be together. Both of us were nervous."

D.A.: "So, having sex with Mr. Grosz on April 12, 1981, wasn't. . . didn't just happen?"

Candy: "That's right. We talked about it before."

D.A.: "Candy, prior to April 12, were you a virgin?"

Candy: (With embarrassment, Candy now speaks for both.) "Yes. So was Mr. Grosz."

D.A.: "Did he tell you that he was a virgin?"

Candy: "Yes. We talked about it."

D.A.: "Did you believe him?"

Candy: "I did."

D.A.: "Thank you, Miss Mills. That's all at this time, Your Honor."

Judge: "Mr. Curtz...?"

At this break from Candy to Curtz, Gabe whispers to him, "Ask her if she loves me." But the lawyer shushes him with, "I'm not going to ask her that. It's not relevant." Gabe accidentally raises his voice. "It's relevant to me."

"It could damage your case," says Curtz brashly and directly into Gabe's ear.

Gabe's final with the comment, "All I want you to do is to ask that question."

But his concern appears at first to be swallowed up by the system. He is about to end and retire his case on a hopeless note, never actually able to connect with anyone, not even his lawyer, on the fact that this is all about love, when the Black female judge impatiently gives Curtz another chance.

She raps her gavel to punish Gabe and Curtz:

Judge: "Counselor, do you or do you not wish to question the witness?

Curtz: "Yes, Your Honor." (He then stands and approaches Candy at her table.) "Candy, you said it was raining when you asked Mr. Grosz to pick you up?"

Candy: "That's right."

Curtz: "What would you have done if he hadn't come to pick you up?

Candy: "I don't know, but I wouldn't have gone back home."

Curtz: "Why not? Wouldn't that have been the smart thing to do?'

D.A.: "Objection. Relevance.

Judge: "Sustained. Mr. Curtz, Miss Mills is not on trial here, and any decision she made on her own is not in question."

Gabe tugs on Curtz's sleeve and mouths the words again, "Ask her," and surprisingly, Curtz relents.

Curtz: "Uh, one last question, Candy. Do you love Mr. Grosz?"

The unusual quality of this question stops the legal flow of thought for everyone. No one questions Curtz's question. Those listening among the crowd seem to hesitate to believe what they hear the lawyer ask. There follows an unnatural pause that adds weight to the reception of Candy's reply.

Candy: "No. I don't."

So blunt, so out of sync. So incorrect, so wrong, so untrue! It is as if Candy takes a bathroom break and is replaced by someone else. Gabe's feelings take a sudden drop to the bottom of a well. The entire case discussion is undermined, and the shiny-shoed bigots in bow ties in the courtroom are assured of the devil's work playing into the souls of this interracial pair.

Curtz: "No further questions, Your Honor."

Whispers shoot through the crowd as the judge reviews the file. No one seems satisfied, not the Mills, not Candy, not Curtz, and least of all, Gabe.

Judge: "Sufficient evidence has been presented by the people to warrant a formal hearing in Superior Court, set for November 9, 1981. Mr. Grosz, I am reminding you that there is a restraining order outstanding, and you are not to have any contact with Miss Mills."

Curtz: "My client understands, Your Honor."

As Gabe and Curtz escort each other out of the courthouse, it occurs to Gabe that this is the opposite of an engagement party. The Mills, the Black Muslims, and a score of others head for their cars in record time, wearing no sign of joy, and Gabe's brief moment with Candy, ensconced by legal personnel in stiff tableau, only makes him feel worse, while Candy appears to be deeply depressed and out of character. To come together this way, rather than to celebrate their plan to marry on her eighteenth birthday, just a few months away, twists his sense of all reasonability.

Least engaged is Curtz, so Gabe asks him flat out, "What happens now?"

"Nothing happens," Curtz suggests flatly. "Your case is moved forward to Superior Court. You're facing a felony charge and possible jail time. If yesterday's incident at your apartment didn't occur, I could've possibly worked out a deal with the Mills. But now, they won't even give me the opportunity to talk to them."

"I'm going to need an additional $5,000 in cash."

"But I don't have $5,000" is all Gabe can say, so painfully without his teaching credential and his job.

This leaves Curtz utterly finished, in a sense the first to leave.

"Then I suggest you find another attorney," he announces. "Listen, I've got another client due in court, and I haven't had breakfast. Give me a call if you come up with the full amount."

At that, Curtz races down the courthouse stairs and into the crowd of the disillusioned. Alone and worse than abandoned, Gabe stops a minute right where he is to sit on the end of the bottom courthouse step and think. He's almost unsure which next step to take or what even is the point of his life these days. His thoughts ring loud and clear. Candy says she does not love me. I'm glad I didn't bring Lily, Mom or Jon with me.

He trudges to his car in a slow and painful fog, accidentally noticing the six Muslims again, all now packed in the same car, watching him. He's further unsettled to see they have the air of stalkers, staring at him like wolves from half-way across the lot.

Candy

In all this disengagement, Gabe has no idea Candy is undergoing a complete breakdown over what she said in court. She feels the same as Gabe but is not allowed to share any words with him. Since it's illegal to call him, write him, or see him, she heads for her local phone booth again the first chance she gets. The following morning she calls the only reliable person she can reach who knows Gabe.

Candy closes the collapsible glass door to the booth, turns away from view, and drops several coins in the slot. She digs into her pocket and pulls out a piece of paper with a phone number scribbled on it, dials and hears the other end ringing. She hears herself speaking much too quickly and in the spirit of begging help but knows this is not a moment for self-control. She has to reach Gabe immediately. She reaches a track coach from another school she barely remembers and says:

"Hello. Is this Mr. Francois Wolman? This is Candy Mills. You met me last year at a track meet. I'm one of Mr. Grosz's athletes—the hurdler. I think you and Gabe were friends in high school? Do you remember me?"

Wolman responds in a straight-forward way.

"The reason I'm calling is because Grosz isn't answering his phone. I testified in court, and . . . I need you to tell him I only said I didn't love him because my parents told me to. They've been really rough on me. I was scared about what they would do."

Wolman remains noncommittal but listens kindly.

"Could you please, sir, tell him that I love him more than ever, and I promise we'll be together. It's real important that he gets this message, very important."

Wolman validates her need without saying if he will or will not convey her message.

"Will you see that he gets it, please?" She speaks repetitively but convincingly, ending in "Oh, thank you, Mr. Wolman. Thank you so much."

Candy hangs up and collapses onto the floor of the booth and breaks out crying hard and long. Eventually, she picks herself up and races back home, where she is supposed to be 24/7, when not at school.

Gabe

Realizing post-court that there's no place to hide, Gabe finally exits the courthouse staircase with the energy of an 80-year-old and the attitude of a Grinch. He's unaccustomed to being in crowds he can't schmooze with, much less this group heading for their cars from the courtroom where he was tried publicly, grimacing at him and none passing the time of day or smiling the way people do who've been at events together.

In a way, he already feels sent to jail, which causes him to flinch over the pain of so much misunderstanding. Why can't people get it that it's all for love, real love, really love?

His family, kindly, never does sit him down over his lovelorn mess and treat him like a child. They never insult Candy, as so many do, including her own parents. They wonder but never say, "What are you getting yourself into?" or "We refuse to accept this Black girl and her dangerous parents!" Lily accepts that Gabe can no longer afford the lawyer she found.

At dinner with a friend-runner, Irving and his wife, Gabe admits being without legal support: "God, Irv, the court case unleashed more problems than solutions. I'm moving into my mom's apartment to save money to try to get a better lawyer. I need a phone at least. Candy sent me an important message, and I didn't get it because I was in the middle of the move. It was about something we had to respond to in court. It was personal and I was upset about what she said. It's important to me to try to figure out what she was saying in court, but we aren't allowed to talk. I need to hear from Candy, and I need a cheaper, better lawyer right away."

Irv puts down his coffee cup with "I have an idea."

He proves the perfect outreach, getting out his phone directory and telling Gabe to set an appointment with Charles Rubin, a sharp criminal attorney he knows well.

"There are decent lawyers who don't charge an arm and a leg. It's a good thing you told me about Curtz. This guy

Rubin's better, and he has a significant clientele, but he's still charging what he always charged. Tell'm what you're up against. I'm pretty sure you can work it out. He's in Westwood too. Hey, stay around here, man!"

Irv is warm-hearted and seems to live in a warm-hearted universe of his own, and he gets Gabe to begin to come out from under a rock and share what he's going to be forced to share one way or another. The next morning Gabe sets an appointment with Rubin.

But coming home to Mom after years on his own is less fun. Aurelie, Mama, seems born to bear the worst, and it's hard for her to project a way out of all of this ever. She doesn't go in and out of Gabe's issue, but stays on it, mostly looking dark in silence and sometimes asking questions. Her life as a Jewish immigrant, leaving Europe under rough times for Jews, has always been a set up for worry. As a mom, she appreciates the opportunity to take Gabe in and "watch his back." She's stirring up old dishes he liked as a kid and sorting out his things that seem to find no place. They're in a homey 50's garden apartment, first-floor, with a guest room, near La Cienega and Olympic. *It's probably*, thinks Gabe, *much less likely to be broken into by Delois and Earl.*

It occurs to Gabe that living with Mama is a bit like using her as a hostage to cover him up as he comes and goes. Who would attack Aurelie? Not the Mills, and God. . . where is his imagination going. . . not the Black Muslims! It feels good coming home to what really is still his home, but he doesn't like the reason he's there.

"Hi, Mama. I found the perfect new lawyer. It's been a good day."

"How's Irv?"

"Great. They're into wok cooking. You should get one."

"Gabe, you got a call from Francois. You know, Francois Wolman. I remember you training him to run faster while he was in high school. The point is, he has some information about Candy."

At the sound of Candy's name, Gabe is on the phone, though it's after 10:00 pm. "Francois, thanks for calling. I'm sorry to call so late, but my mom says you know something about Candy."

"I do. I do. I'm glad you're with your mom right now. Yeah. Well, Candy called me. I guess she can't call you. You stay on her man, watch her from afar if ya can, 'cause she's low, really low right now."

"I know," Gabe adds. "That's why I called you right away.

"She's a bright and assured young lady, but I think she was about to fold up when she was talking to me."

"What'd she say?" Gabe's sweating a bit and listening hard.

"Well, this is a strange thing for me to say to you, but I'm quoting her. Have you got that? Okay, exactly what she said is, "Tell him that I love him more than ever, and I promise we'll be together."

Gabe tears up, sweats more, and momentarily says nothing at all. Aurelie, standing next to him, does the same, as if their eyes were all part of one person. She silently gives him a questioning look, and he thanks Francois for playing a role that is going to hold him together.

"G'night, Francois. I owe you one. I really, really do, guy. Bye."

In the morning Rubin is reached, and apprised on the phone of what Gabe's case entails, and doors immediately unlock. Rubin says to collect letters of support, so Gabe later talks to his former employer from his high school days, a boss he trusted, Marty Levitt, who owns Laurel Hardware in West Hollywood, and he's offered and takes a hardware sales job.

The next ring is . . . CANDY! She's working part-time downtown at the *LA Times* selling subscriptions. She uses their phone to call him and asks to meet right away at 7th and Flower near the Plaza.

Gabe's there in thirty minutes, parked and striding at a hardy pace through the hustle and bustle of the downtown streets. Ahead, he sees Candy sitting on a concrete bench in a tiny green patch next to an office building. She sees him too and they find each other instantly, closing in a big, long hug.

"What are we doing? Sometimes breathing seems illegal," Candy says.

"I know," says Gabe. "When the phone rings, I freeze every time. It's so good to see you, though."

"Gabe, did you understand from my phone message that I froze in court, with my parents staring me down? There were some real threats from them beforehand. The only reason I didn't say 'I love you' then was because of them."

Gabe rests from the inside out to hear this. He looks up at the sky in an act similar to a prayer of thankfulness.

"Are you okay at your mom's?" Candy asks. "For a while, I didn't know where you were. Mr. Wolman told me you moved."

"It's good to be with Mama, She's even worse than me about everything, but she never says anything bad about you. We're all going to sit this thing out. Curtz and I have split, but I think I may have a better lawyer. That's the next nightmare to unravel."

"I'm worried for you about your money."

"I know. Me too, but I've got a hardware store job now. At least I've got a phone again. But these lawyers are right. You're in danger talking to me."

"Well, I'd say you're in more danger talking to me! Don't worry. I'll always love you, Baby. . . no matter where we are or what's going on."

Gabe raises Candy by the arm. She lands a kiss on his cheek, and they walk up Seventh Street toward the Plaza.

"Candy, we're all wondering how you're holding up?"

"Some days are better than others," she says. "You know I'm no longer going to Jefferson? A lot of the kids were giving me a hard time about my testimony, so I transferred to Dorsey. My mother doesn't get so mad at me anymore because she thinks you and I haven't talked. She has no idea that I'm with you today. Anyway, I told her that I'm going to marry you—no matter what she does—as soon as I'm 18."

"What'd she say to that?"

"That our kids'll be deformed."

"Oh, real nice. You know, maybe everybody's right."

"About what?"

"That I'm crazy."

As they reach the Plaza, a Black Muslim, smartly dressed in a black suit and tie, recognizes Gabe and Candy from court. He accosts them, stopping them dead in their tracks at the entrance to the Plaza. He grabs hold of Candy's arm. "Do your parents know you're associating with this White devil? You ought to be ashamed. You know that Black and White aren't allowed to mix. You're embarrassing the Black race."

Gabe tugs at the man's muscular grip with, "Let'r go!"

"Get your motherfuck'n hands off me, Cracker. Don't ever lay White hands on a member of the Nation of Islam!"

Gabe, trying to shift to words, looks the thug in the eye with, "This is none of your business."

"Listen, Peckerwood, the Nation of Islam looks out for its own. A sister Judge ordered you to stay away from this girl. Now get your honky ass back to your White world before I kick it around the block."

Candy, held and unable to get free, says, "Let me go. I'm gonna scream."

But the bigot jerks her inside the main door to the Plaza and shouts instead, "Security! Shoplifter!"

Gabe jumps him from behind; Candy breaks loose, and he grabs her hand with "Come on," and they bolt together down the busy street. Horns sound, tires squeal, and the attacker takes off after them, weaving through traffic, onto the sidewalk, and a chase is on.

Gabe looks back and sees the Black Muslim gaining on him, grabs Candy's hand, and steers her around a corner. They take off along the sidewalk, maneuvering through pedestrians. But the stalker rounds the corner, shoving people out of his way, as he kicks into high gear. They push behind a thick shrub and eye each other in agreement.

"Okay Baby," says her coach. "Let's put it into high gear and show'm who the real runners are."

They wait, she beams, and they're off on one more glorious runners' high. They lose the stalker, and finally erase his image in less than two minutes. The sweaty winners fall into an ice-cream shop and land on two high round, swirly stools.

"Ice-cream?" asks Gabe. "Ice-cream, ice-cream, we all scream for ice-cream!"

They decide to sing it, victorious as ever, wiping off their sweat and ending one more stolen escape together, this time in a big, sloppy kiss.

"We always win," says Candy, catching her breath, while Gabe smacks her on the back in congratulations.

"We're a winning team, remember that."

It's hard to believe this hide 'n seek game that's so irresistible is so dangerous. After the Black Muslim incident, the runner-lovers are afraid to meet together in public anymore. At least, once Gabe reaches Rubin's law office for a second try at legal defense, Rubin seems genuinely happy to meet Gabe, despite all he already knows about the case. He's a shot in the arm for Gabe.

Candy

After Candy's loss of Jefferson, Gabe, track, and hurdling, it's a surprise visit of Dawn and Juana from her old track team that makes the only positive day on her season's calendar. Besides homework and dodging her mother's evil eye, the only thing Candy's doing in her last two and a half months before the awaited eighteenth birthday is more singer-songwriting on the family porch. Under the shady cabana, she belts out choppy lines in a style half Janis Joplin and half Billie Holiday. But Dawn and Juana sidle into the yard and catch her, cracking up to hear her reeling out:

> Young sinners, where will you go?
> —Paradise don't—
> —Live here no more—

The girls chime in, laughing their heads off.

Dawn says, "We know that one. Are you on the same song? You've lost your edge!"

"Hell, no," says Candy. She jumps up, more than relieved to see the two, anybody from her old school in months. "No, no. There's more. Catch this whole thing together." Then she opens with:

> Young sinners
> Where will you go?
> Paradise don't live here
> No more.
> Young sinners
> What will you do?
> Not a dime in your pocket
> A heart full o' blues.

"Cool enough," says Dawn.

"Sounds true. You an' your mom celebrat'n the blues stars that left this gangland for—God, where did they go? N'awlins? That was twenty years ago. I vote we all leave. I'm ready. Crips ain't play'n no decent music. In fact, something happened to my school. There ain't no girls track anymore, no trophies, no mean ass coach with a heart of gold."

"Quit complaining," says Juana. "It's not Candy's fault. "

"Okay. You've always been her best friend," says Dawn. "I never blame you, Candy. We just really miss you, both of you. You've always been crazy, you and Grosz, but it's crazier without you two . . . frankly depressing."

"Couldn't you've stayed til the end of the semester?" Juana asks Candy. "I guess it was pretty bad, some of the things kids were saying behind your back, and the look on your face. We knew you were hurt."

"But Dorsey, our arch-rival?" Dawn throws in. "Were you try'n to get even with us or what? If you were try'n to get even, you'd be runn'n for Dorsey."

"Hey," answers Juana. "I can answer for you, girl! Not everybody falls for the seductive garbage an' stuff, and nobody believes Grosz's a sex offender. I think it's just, this is sleaze town, and the most amazing thing's that nobody's shot Grosz yet."

"That's why he's not here," Candy says. "And I think my mom's still trying to get my dad to kill'm. We live an underground existence, and I'm not even pregnant, drunk, dumb, or anything. Neither is Grosz. If I can sneak in on'm ever, we just run, read Thoreau, and watch sitcoms."

"Well, you sing good," says Dawn. "Is this your new sport?"

Gradually, Candy, becoming relaxed and relieved, breaks into another of her songs, "Modern Slave Girl."

"This one's for all of us," she says, throwing out deep, strong chords of:

> Modern-day slave girl
> Your house is not your home
> Moder -day slave girl
> You can do better on your own.

After a round of lemonade, the three huddle up closer on the porch swing and Delois' porch rocker.

"Does it bother you, not competing?" Juana says, getting up and rubbing her friend's shoulders.

The thought ends Candy's singing and is frankly unbearable for her. She doesn't answer; just looks the girls right in their eyes with pain. It's good enough communication, and the subject changes.

"At least we got here to tell you how we feel, how everybody feels. What happened is okay with us," says Dawn. "Crazy as it was, it makes sense."

"Yeah," Juana adds. "If it was me, I'd wanta know my friends are okay with what I'm about."

This teary point throws the three together in a massive hug, and there seems to be nothing else crucial to deliver.

"We always look up to you," Juana finishes.

After the girls leave, Candy stops her singing, goes inside, and falls into her bed with her old gold 'n green Jefferson Democrats pillows, and drifts off into an afternoon nap, remembering easier times, but never forgetting Gabe, the goal of her life.

Gabe

While Candy sinks into her happiest dreams since she left Jefferson, Gabe moves on from his stupefied first lawyer to his runner friend Irv's suggestion, the well-known Charles Rubin. Gabe has no idea what he's walking into, penniless and discredited, not to mention lacking insight into his situation, the one thing a lawyer needs most to build a case.

But few could've shaken him inside out as needed as well as Rubin, who exhibits the altruism to handle significant pro bono cases and to, as in Gabe's situation, take a smaller fee from certain clients and dig hard enough to develop cases that appear lacking. While Gabe continues to mumble that "It was all for love," a less than legal consideration, Rubin gains Gabe's confidence, relaxes him, and finally pulls out pure gold for the case, offering real hope.

Who knew that by 1989 the beloved and trusted Rubin, the criminal lawyer who opened his first private practice in his matter of fact suite on Wilshire in Beverly Hills in 1970, would become the same Charles Rubin, Head Judge of the Supreme Court of Beverly Hills. He became famous for high successful settlement rates in thousands of cases, including the three-week debacle in court with Zsa Zsa Gabor over her driving without a license with an open flask of Jack Daniels, ending in her slapping the cop who arrested her.

The Charles Rubin who takes a minute for our down-trodden anti-hero in 1981 later rides out the media storm of a Kardashian-style celebrity, complete with a bomb threat and has been forever hailed for halting Gabor's art-sketching of jurors as inappropriate court room demeanor.

As Gabe enters Rubin's seventh floor, small, two-room office, he is full of confidence in his friend Irv who sent him and thinking about just how much he may have in savings to pay for better legal help. Rubin is similarly open to the moment, but unaware of the possibilities for the case and is not yet famous in his field. They are unknowingly a match made in heaven.

Gabe sits in a fold-up chair next to a potted plant and bookcase in the reception room that has no window. He's wearing clothes comfortable to run in after he leaves. Rubin enters in an off the rack, tired-looking suit and pulls the runner heartily into his office that is mostly desk.

"Hey, sit right here," Rubin says. "Sorry we toss the coffee after ten am. It just doesn't last. Well, let's start out with a little summary, your own summary of what hap-pened to you to explain this arrest."

Gabe edges forward from a surprisingly comfortable suede desk lounger to, for the first time, spell it all out: "We worked together as coach and athlete for about a year and a half," he starts, putting down his paper cup of water." And we fell in love. Candy's 17, and also, . . . if it matters, . . .she's Black."

Rubin's eyebrows raise, and Gabe continues: "We had a sexual encounter two weeks before her parents found out about us. I was suspended from my teaching position. Then I was charged with statutory rape. Not long after that, Candy called me early one morning and said she didn't want to go back home,   and I picked her up and brought her to my apartment. That same evening, her parents broke into my apartment and took her back home. To make things worse, she testified against me, and that's when my lawyer told me to find another attorney."

Oddly, Gabe omits the mention of Candy's dad's break-in-entry and physical attack.

At this, Rubin gets out of his chair and starts to slowly pace the tiny room.

He says, "You know, Mr. Grosz, I've been practicing law for over 15 years, and I thought I'd heard it all. But this. . ." He stops and pulls a charm out of his pocket, looks at it, and rubs it, "This takes the cake. I mean, I've handled rapes, murders, assaults, but never anything quite like this." He pauses to consider, then moves on with, "Okay, what else?"

As a result of several intense recent weeks of violence and confusion, Gabe answers immediately and firmly, looking straight into Rubin's eyes, "I've been thinking about changing my plea from not guilty to guilty."

This changes the entire momentum. Rubin instantly jabs at the suffering anti-hero in the way that war buddies rant together about death jokes.

"Are you kidding?" he plants on Gabriel.

"But if I plead innocent, won't that mean I'm denying the relationship and I don't love her?"

Gabe says this, not looking at Rubin, but at the floor, and Rubin's response sounds like God out of a cloud, resonating with enough truth to halt everything that has gone on, is going on, and could still go on.

Rubin quotes Shakespeare. "'Romeo, Romeo, thou art wedded to calamity.'" In doing so, Rubin repeats a thought that has already become a common dark one in Gabe's life.

"I've had the thought," says Gabe.

"You're over-thinking. Where did you get that idea? If we ever get you out of this thing, you should teach ethics instead of track!"

Gabe, speaking more quickly than before, starts revealing his feelings. "I want to show Candy's parents they're wrong about my intentions."

"Slow down. Look, what good will you do her in prison? I'm not going to let you change your plea! Do you understand?"

"It was hard for her to testify. I don't want her to have to go through that experience again," says Gabe, still thinking and acting like her wise, older coach and protector, though by now it is clear she is no weaker than he and more likely to survive a worst case scenario.

"Where are you getting your information?" the lawyer aks.

"Well, first she called a friend, then she called me—."

Rubin interrupts. "You talk to her?"

"She calls me."

"She calls you? So hang up. You have to get a grip on yourself, Gabe. You're not Bonnie and Clyde. She's not Patty Hearst at the hideout the cops burned down in South Central. Weren't you instructed not to have contact with each other?"

"Well, I love her, and you know, she also said we're not Bonnie and Clyde. I see what you mean. But I love her. That's what just doesn't work with this whole thing. Nobody sees it. It's not about legality or job contract. There's no Thanksgiving dinner with her parents where I can ask for her hand."

"Your love is more like a death wish. I'm a good attorney, but you're digging your own grave with a bulldozer, and you expect me to get you out with a teaspoon." Rubin utters these pronouncements with a new and heavy sense that begins to explain why the previous lawyer threw in the rag.

Gabe says, "I could have prevented all this, everything. I didn't think about the consequences. Now she's having a hard time at home and at school, losing her scholarships, track glory, and friends."

Rubin the realist responds, bouncing his harsh words off the close walls: "But she's not the one facing four years in prison!"

"Okay, Sir! I do need a new approach."

"Right. Make sure you bring your toothbrush. You'll need it."

"Am I really going to prison?"

The dark-humored lawyer winks. "Bring your toothpaste too."

"This is not funny, is it?" Gabe begins to murmur.

The two observe a well-earned silence here, needed for each to absorb the shock of what the other said, but a silent commitment emerges that seems relatively indestructible. Each seems to respect where the other is coming from and the two universes meld into the necessary full reality. Rubin knows he pulls decent clients out of moments of insanity, and Gabe knows his weaknesses are showing and he needs support to articulate what he cannot explain.

Rubin's hungry and senses Gabe hasn't eaten well since he last saw Candy, so he throws out the legal point du jour and pushes a somewhat weakened Gabe toward the elevator to the cafe on floor three. "So, have you got it? You have to keep out of further trouble. You're going to keep away from her."

"I have to try," Gabe answers, somehow also sensing he hasn't eaten much in the last year and a half. "I love her, and I've never loved anyone in my life. Why is that making me hungry? You know, I feel like having a huge chef's salad, some marinated trout, and a raspberry smoothie!"

"What you need is your first double cheeseburger with fries and a malt."

While they fight over which foods can truly sustain Gabe, the accused and counsel eat well and move onto camaraderie rarely reached in law offices. A liaison is formed between Gabe's unfettered soul and Rubin's bright ploys.

Round II in the Halls of Justice

Rubin aptly adopts Gabe's "all for love" view of the case, translating his pure schmaltz into legalese. In a matter of days, he prepares and mails a letter from his office to Candy's parents. While it reeks of legal parchment stationery and business formal language, suggesting a required reading and careful consideration, it amounts to "My client did it all for love."

Rubin grasps Gabe's desire to win hearts and minds but realizes this can only be achieved here by cloaking feelings under the auspices of the law. His letter reminds the Mills that the law takes into consideration excellence of background, moral history, and intention. Without mentioning love, he lists Gabe's intention of marriage to their daughter after her eighteenth birthday, etc.

This letter swims almost instantly from Westwood, 20 miles south-east, to South Central. Candy always brings the mail to her mom and is the first person in the Mills' house to see the snitty-looking envelope. Who, what? A Westwood attorney? The first thing she does is stuff it into a drawer in her bedroom. Later, after entertaining a build-up of scary fantasies of how her parents would react to a confrontation of any kind from Gabe's defense team, she burns it in the alley behind the house and sweeps up after herself.

All this happens exactly as the two White guys on the other side of town who plan this generous moment of spirit are congratulating themselves on opening doors to understanding interracial coupling, ageism, and personal vs. academic freedom. They fantasize the Mills dropping by to shake hands and drop the charges. In fact, only years later does Candy reveal why they never receive any response to this first of Rubin's bright ploys. The second ploy, however, after some time and effort, proves the breaking point that can save Gabe in court.

Rubin says, "Just think. Think hard of anything that happened, anything you possess that we can use to prove how consensual Candy was. I know you don't want her pressured in court again, and her parents prevent her from taking your side under any circumstances, but you yourself might have something to prove consensual intent. Scour your stuff, even if it's all in boxes at your mom's house."

Rubin always knows when to insist, and sometime later Gabe finds some letters that he reads very carefully until—"Oh, there it is—one line: "Gabe, I want you to be the first man I ever have sex with." He finds it, and what a great piece of evidence! Not only is it exactly what Rubin needs, it also is an example of the virgin backgrounds of these two, helping erase some suspicion of their lifestyles. At this point, Rubin is ready for the case and happily still trying to get Gabe to drink malts and insult his track diet with French fries.

Gabe stands steadier than he has, not only because of the build-up of his case, but because he learns Candy and her parents will not be in the court room next time. He also doubts he'll sit side by side with the Black Muslims again. Massaging his brain with these positive thoughts, he's pulled away from his hardware store counter on the job for a personal call from Candy, calling from a public phone at her new school, Dorsey High.

She stuffs her lunch sandwich between texts and her notebook in her back hall locker and runs past student crowds all the way to the only pay-phone. She drops in a quarter. "Hello. May I speak to Gabriel Grosz, please? Tell him it's Candy. Thank you . . . Yes, I know he is an employee at work, but this is a very important call."

Gabe, standing behind a store counter in West Hollywood, at Laurel Hardware, in his store apron, is ringing up a purchase. The customer gathers his things and walks out, when Gabe hears someone in the back yell: "Hey, Gabe! Phone. Someone named Candy."

At once, Gabe races to the back and grabs the receiver from the clerk, who squints at him. "Let me know if there's anything else I can do."

"Hi Candy!" Just hearing his own words shocks Gabe into a moment of excitement.

"Gabe. God, it's you!" Candy starts to lose it. Her planned two-minute call turns instantly into emotional mush. "How is it—the hardware store?"

"Fine. Not bad. Good people. Where are you calling from?"

"From Dorsey. I went by your apartment, but you're not there anymore, and I don't know where your mom lives. I keep thinking about your case and you getting your job back somehow."

"Just keep your team spirit up. I have a new, cool lawyer."

At this point, the two are interrupted by a clerk in the front yelling, "We need another clerk up here!"

"Hell, I have to get back to work right now, Candy."

"Okay, bye Baby. Don't forget, I'll be 18 in five months, April 26th."

"I know. I have it marked on my . . ."

They're interrupted again from the front of the store. "Gabe, come on!"

Candy sobs a sound she can't even hear herself, as the school bell hammers mercilessly, ending the lunch period. It rattles the entire hall, leaving her to hang up and choose between—getting her sandwich out of her locker and skipping class—or going to class and skipping lunch.

Gabe's back at his counter, but a different man.

"Who was that?" the clerk asks.

"Sorry, my girl," he answers with a new and funny grin on his face that must belong to people who eat more than he used to.

Somehow, Gabe begins to feel he's not alone, and he may have a future someday, Candy is not an apparition of some ancient muse of love who sweeps in and out of shadows and clouds, but a real person with a birthday soon and a bright future. He thinks to bring Rubin a brown bag health lunch. It feels really solid to have him also "on the team."

Candy's call intended to wish him well in court, but he doesn't need it because he feels it can happen now. He can fantasize about returning one day to his Jefferson colleagues and classes with some acceptance, but he cannot imagine it without them saying, "How did you pull it off?" He doesn't know what to do next, but the thought that Candy and Rubin are both on his side, two of the smartest and most skilled people he's ever met, starts to feel like a game he'd be happy to coach.

Miracle Court

Gabe's newfound optimism plays on his mind as he parks on November 7th, 1981, at the Santa Monica Superior Court. He sees Rubin pulling out his briefcase from his front seat and meets him enthusiastically in the lot. There will be no one from the Mills' household this time hence a quieter, more private procedure. It strikes Gabe that, after growing up not far from the part of LA called The Miracle Mile, today could prove an extension of his life to move through "Miracle Court." Of course, his heart is in his throat, but Rubin is hearty as ever, and their plot is nearly on the table.

"Yo," says Rubin. "Now, you take a look at what you two did. That sack of love letters from Candy you found at your mom's is evidence of the consensual nature of your relationship, and Candy's erudition supports her decisions with logic. And, God, she even wrote you one letter in French! . . . This story is not only too romantic for the average courtroom; it speaks to an intellectual connection. They can't throw this stuff out. In fact, it's quite a read.

Hey, Gabe, when this is over and you're ready to write a screenplay about your story, can I do it?"

Rubin's good nature puts Gabe in a good mood. Gabe answers with swagger, "Sure."

"Well, I'm not kidding. This should be a non-fiction novel, and I brought a sheet for Consent of Right to Authorship for you to sign if you feel like it."

"Can't think of anyone I'd rather have write it," Gabe answers, surprised at his own attitude, considering the danger as well as the fun of entering the court room now to change his plea and present the message—as he always wanted but never was able to before.

Gabe helps Rubin carry in copious materials, and the two settle in before Judge David Fitts, a sixtyish, White judge at the bench. This courtroom at Santa Monica Superior Court is relatively quiet and beaming with light and shiny floors.

It's October 7th, 1981, five months before Candy's liberating birthday. With no real looky-loos at hand and just a few legal assistants coming and going with messages and paperwork, the distinguished Judge Fitts, who years earlier became famous for his decision in the Sirhan Sirhan Case regarding the assassination of Bobby Kennedy, strikes his gavel with determination.

"Proceedings begin on the case of Gabriel Grosz, accused of the felony charge of Penal Code 261.5C, illegal sexual intercourse. Mr. Grosz, I've been a judge for many years, and in all those years, I must admit I've never come across a case quite like this one. Frankly, I don't exactly know what to make of it. Personally, I feel it belongs more on Dear Abby's desk than in my court."

At this, the DA shifts notably in her chair, looking wide-eyed into Judge Fitts' face as if wanting to interrupt him.

"However, be that as it may, we're here to determine if a crime has been committed, and I'll base my judgement on that and that alone."

The judge quickly leafs through some papers. Fitts continues tediously adding an intimate background to Gabe's case that continues to swing the decision back in favor of Gabe.

"I've never met the young lady involved, but after reading the letters and poems she wrote to you, Mr. Grosz, it is clear that she is a very bright young lady."

Gabe's habit of shifting from lover to coach enters at the slightest mention of Candy's potential, and his posture now takes on a professional turn beyond that of the D.A., as if he'd been asked for a recommendation for his runner, health student, and legendary team player. But he knows to stay silent, just nodding repeatedly, acting less like a miserable accused felon than a reliable witness.

Fitts continues, "I was especially impressed by the letter she wrote to you in French. It is quite clear what her feelings are for you. I've reviewed the charges made against you, Mr. Grosz, and I see that you've decided to change your 'not guilty' plea to 'no contest,' which is agreeable with the District Attorney's office. I've also read the report sent to me by the Probation Department, and I'll get to that in a minute. At this juncture, I feel the relationship you had with the young lady was mutual and consenting, free of criminal or malicious intent."

The D.A. starts whispering into her colleague's ear. Fitts resumes with, "However, Mr. Grosz, you were sexually involved with a minor."

There is a lull throughout the court. At this point, all eyes fix on Fitts and where his meandering train of thought will land.

"This, Counselor and Mr. Grosz, constitutes a commitment of a crime. I do not feel that in this case, however, a felony conviction would be appropriate, but the law has indeed been broken. And because of this, I feel it's a misdemeanor conviction that is justified!"

"Your Honor," the D.A. breaks in. "We accept the change from felony to misdemeanor."

Rubin, at this point, calmly and with assurance raises his hand silently and is summoned to the bench. He spends five minutes quickly navigating some points on papers already held by the judge. Fitts duly notes the suggested material, and the two mumble back and forth agreeably, though they cannot be heard. He turns to the D.A. as Rubin returns to his seat.

"Duly noted, Counselor, as are the extensive and quite explanatory materials submitted by the Defense. I am also fully aware that the young lady's parents wanted prison time as the law stipulates. But given the circumstances of this case, I feel that three years probation and a $360.00 fine is an appropriate and fair judgement."

Gabe, who has been sitting up straight and on edge, falls back loudly into the leather folds of his chair, breaking the dead silence of astonishment of all. Whispers follow the judgement on both sides, and Fitts pauses to allow for the reaction, aware of the effect of his decision. He signals the court reporter to stop transcribing, and the case is closed.

The D.A. and company gather their files and briefcases with no further conversation or comment and begin to exit the courtroom. Fitts calls Gabe and Rubin to his desk.

"Strictly off the record, Mr. Grosz, let me suggest to you that you get your life back on track and stay away from this girl, at least until she's of legal age. And for your sake stay away from her parents. If you see them on the road, my advice to you is to cross the street and avoid them at all cost."

Knowing how difficult this advice is to follow, Gabe nods politely without reply and backs off, saying, "Thank you, Your Honor."

Gabe and Rubin save their hugs and exaltation for the parking lot. Rubin, ever concerned Gabe is not eating enough, hands him a box lunch saved from the back seat of his car.

"I know you'll turn down a celebration lunch to go sit by your phone and wait for some kind of illegal call. Keep me out of it, Buddy, but you know what? I'm thrilled for both of you and know you're just five months from the real celebration."

He shakes Gabe's hand only to find out Gabe has prepped a box lunch for Rubin too.

"Try it," Gabe says. "It'll put hair on your chest, sunflower seeds, a sesame bar, vegan cheese and spinach salad. Skip the beer."

"I only put one beer in yours," Rubin says. "It'll clean out your gut. What am I saying about guts? You're the gutsy one here. You'd better keep me posted."

"Absolutely. We'll probably name all our children after you—Charles, Charlene. Well, two kids are enough."

"Get outa here. Go live your life. Keep the soap opera outa the courts. I enjoyed it. Bye."

Oddly, the D.A. is Gabe's next and last encounter. In the parking lot, the D.A. approaches him. "Mr. Grosz," she says, grabbing him by the arm. "You did know that a previous pre-trial meeting was held when you were not here?"

"No, I didn't know that."

"Well, I just want to wish you well. Judge Fitts, your attorney, and I agreed before the trial started that you are no criminal. I agreed as well, but, as you probably observed, it is my duty to act as prosecutor throughout."

Stunned with appreciation, Gabe remains silent, as the D.A. continues.

"Just one thing, for your own sake. Do not speak to Candace at all, under any circumstances. We'd all like to see you get this thing behind you."

At this, all leave in their cars, Gabe somewhat numb with success, sad only to have to hold his joy from the one he loves for. . . does it really have to be five more months?

As for the long-term effect of the case, Rubin and Fitts are never to be forgotten, and following their futures among America's best-known men of law adds heart to Gabe's memories. They not only excel as judges (which Rubin eventually became), but they move into and stay in the national limelight, Rubin taking his altruism and unusual commitment to TV and radio lectures and his glamor into his Beverly Hills wedding to a James Bond super-actress in 1991. Of course, his jailing of Zsa Zsa Gabor remains his steamiest and most publicly beloved achievement.

Fitts' prosecution as assistant D.A., at an earlier part of his career in 1968 of Sirhan Sirhan for the murder of Bobby Kennedy, launched him toward his judgeship for his uncanny ability to handle Sirhan with the same delicacy he applied to Gabe's case. Both Gabe and Sirhan's stories were outside of the box with multiple psychological and contradictory complexities which Fitts handles with instant insight.

Interfacing with the violent drama of South Central, the challenges of the Black diaspora that Candy's mother takes on for her family—wandering from East to West and North to South in search of opportunity for her children, Gabe is aware his survival came from the heroes in his midst, who were all around him, including his patient mom who'd fled her Hungarian-Jewish heritage in Eastern Europe at a difficult time, only to have to put up with seeing Gabe take on new cultural challenges of his own.

"You won," she said. "You're a winner."

"It's all for love, Mom. That's all I ever said."

"You know it was wrong, Gabe. She's Black, and you were her teacher."

"I know. I do know. But now it's a new story."

Back at the ranch for Candy and Gabe is still a lot like jail. Gabe's finally released from the threat of a jail term, but now it's a jail-like existence for both of them. Their first-time lovers' passion is illegal until Candy's birthday, five months ahead. And worse, they are still not allowed to communicate at all, even by phone or letter.

Neither is comfortable going backwards, but Gabe and his community are relatively stoic, accepting, and supportive, while the hell that Candy created for herself is rather like Hester Prinn's in *The Scarlet Letter*. She is a marked woman at 17 and expected by everyone but Gabe to apologize, change her ways, and amend her life. Instead, she hides out quietly at another unfamiliar high school, cuts her athletic competition and social life, and does homework in her bedroom, on good days, she composes and sings torch songs on her porch.

How does Gabe talk to her about his release from the felony conviction? How do they celebrate this victorious first step toward their future? Do they have a secret interlocutor to speak to each side from each side? No, but they should. Looking back on our own first passionate love stories, we probably remember, as much as the drive for love, the mindlessness surrounding it and how unimportant almost anything else seemed, how poorly we handled anything requiring mature complex thought, and—how many mistakes we made because "love is blind."

Candy does, of course, hear Gabe's court news but not from anyone. The court decision comes to her parents in a letter from Superior Court. Her mom brings it in through their yard, so full of flowers of every kind, so the place Candy likes to escape to! Delois notices immediately where the mail is from and slams the door behind her recklessly, shutting out the sun and flowers, already prepared to vent her feelings again. Candy, spread out on the couch with a textbook, watches her mom open the letter and react.

"He got off!" Delois rages at the top of her voice. She marches directly to Candy and waves the notice in her face. "He changed his goddam plea and got off! You know what that means, huh?"

"No," says Candy, hoping not to be hit.

"It means he got away with it. That's what. Three years' probation and a $300 fine! The man is not going to jail. That's what you're worth—three hundred dollars." She rubs the letter in Candy's face, now glazed with tears and stiff with pain. "Three—hundred—dollars!" Delois yells again and pulls a yank of Candy's hair hard enough to throw her down to the floor. "You hussy, whore!" She grabs her on the floor, both hands around her neck.

"Ma, you're choking me," Candy says, trying to pull back up. "I can't. . . breathe."

Suddenly, Earl rushes into the room. "Lois, stop. She's not worth it. She's just a cheap little tramp." He tugs with both hands, and Delois lets go. Candy rolls to her feet and runs to her room.

Gabe does not hear for years about these incidents that happen to Candy at home. In their peculiar five-month detention, Candy's more dangerous agonies are not known or shared. But Gabe worries about her and has always in the past, legal or not, responded when she begged his help.

Gabe's five months of waiting are embarrassing and hard to deal with, but any hinted blame is tame. His inner circle knows he's lovelorn over a girl with problems and that things are not going well. They wish he'd make another choice, but they know he's not a sexual aggressor, and like the crowd in South Central, they suspect Candy, also lovelorn, is the one who lit the match. As Judge Fitts suggests, Candy and Gabe present a soap opera evoking our compassion more than ridicule.

Jon has stopped his long runs along the golf greens, swearing his psychiatric advice runs too slow for the pace of his friend's jump into the soup. Irv is pleased to have helped find a good lawyer but worries over the idea of bringing Candy's family history into their own. Gabe's mom begins to feel the issues of ethnicity that caused her to escape Eastern Europe may racaially haunt Gabe here in America. If he marries Candy, she tells him she will babysit their children if they look White but not if they look Black.

Amid all this, Gabe is thankful for his full-time hardware store job, offered by a supportive friend. He knows he's several steps at least away from ever regaining his teaching career, but putting his "nose to the grindstone," he rebuilds his resume toward a return to coaching. When does he miss Candy the most? When he's running. When does she miss him most? When she's running, when her inner voice always screams out to her —"I'm running without a coach, my love, my Gabe." They're still both running daily, but they're running lonely.

Candy

In 1981, emancipation for interracial couples is real but slow-moving. The Lovings from the D.C. area took the brunt of the nation's distaste in 1967, achieving a Supreme Court decision in their favor that made interracial marriages legal across the nation. But even today the choice is considered nouveau, and the concept of living in a comfortably integrated American neighborhood is often more of a wish than a promise. The Lovings, were pulled out of their marital bed by local cops, with Mrs. Loving, the Black bride, jailed for cohabitation, putting in most of the hard work. Candy scan see the future she's beginning to prepare for won't be easy either.

Tuesday, April 25,1982, the day before her birthday, the day before she plans to break out of her domicile and the shadow of Jefferson High in South Central, the day before she is finally with Gabe again, she thinks, she writes songs, and she sings. And her last-ditch social action is to slouch on by Jefferson High for a final run of laps where she learned from Gabe to become a first-class runner. Someday, she hopes, Gabe will be forgiven for being her coach and allowed to coach again. Someday their ages will not seem so far apart. But racially she feels they will spend a lifetime standing up straight and watching each other's back.

Candy plants herself on her beloved front porch swing, probably for the last time, and stretches out slowly and widely, eyes to the sky, allowing some last moments of appreciation for the best of what has transpired in her last 18 years there, and she makes a major decision before leaving. *Just call me Billee* she tells herself. She formally creates a singer-song-writer nickname she uses for the rest of her life.

She has Billie Holiday's records and a lot from other jazz folks from the Dunbar Club right down the street, now only the historic remnant of what the 4206 Central Avenue 40's music scene had been. Iin 1981 it still has its arched windows and balconies with grillwork. The original Billee was the same, a troubled, talented New Yorker with high points in her career life right in Candy's neighborhood. Both Billies had full faces and stunning energy. The Black jazz elite simply did not skip South Central. They were there, and in years to come, Candy decides she will tell the same story. She will leave tomorrow, but hold onto her sport and her song, South Central's gifts to her.

She sings Rodgers and Hart's "Blue Moon:"

Blue Moon—you saw me standing alone
Without a dream in my heart
Without a love of my own.
Blue Moon—you knew
just what I was there for
Someone I really could care for...

As if responding to the real Billie, Candy pumps out new lyrics of her own and writes them down, humming along. She changes her shoes and shirt and jogs slowly and nostalgically over to the Jefferson High she was forced to flee. It looks different like an almost thing-of-the-past. She has schoolwork due, but thankfully no longer for the teachers she sees. She notices the little park attached to the athletic field more than ever before. It seems a great place to sit down and sort out what you're carrying. She thinks she can't remember any other campus with an attached park like that. The track looks luscious, having spent a whole semester away from that sort of thing. The lanes are bright and look well-tended. She jumps up to run the track, when—oh—God! Somebody grabs her, and she falls.

"Well, if it ain't Ms. Track Star! I'm gonna help you back up, you huzzy. You sure ain't help'n us, your old school, this year!"

Candy recognizes Jesse, a sophomore not on any teams at school. "Look, Jesse," she says. "What'd you do for me this year? I'm doing double-time just for being famous, and you're over here just tripping up girls. Don't you have anything better to do?" She brushes herself off and checks for scratches and bruises.

"Shit. You're right. I haven't got a single date trip'n girls, and I know you're not available. Wanna coke from the machine?"

"Not from you," Candy banters back.

"Sure not. You want the ice tea. I know, you plan on college hurdles and clean liv'n. Well, I'm sorry. If you take a bench, I'll serve ya, and I'll tell ya some'm."

Candy in her accepting, nostalgic state takes a bench and stares at the lame character beside her who hasn't even been a Jeffersonian long enough to learn how to talk to girls or to sound cool.

Halfway through her free drink, Jesse stares her down and states flat out: "It's spite. The whole thing's spite. You shoulda been Prom Queen, but instead you snubbed us all and walked away with the teacher. We know we lost and he won, and you know what? It's right. You guys are the best we ever knew, and you should hang together and get outa here."

"Really, Jesse?" she answers. "That's the sweetest thing anybody ever said to me at Jefferson or Dorsey."

Candy gives Jesse a warm sock in the chest and sits alone for some minutes after he takes off with his friend who comes by. She thinks, *Well, no matter, I do enjoy mumbling along with the imbeciles around here. There's nobody to talk to, period, at Dorsey.*

Candy's moment of school reunion thoughts is amazingly rosy. She's surprised at her feeling of closure. Though she has two more months before graduation at Dorsey, the thought of closing the chapter in the hood feels almost as good as it feels bad. She does not cry on the outside, only on the inside.

It's mere hours until she turns 18. So once again, separating her outside self from her inside self, she does what's needed for tomorrow morning for her escape from home forever, prepping things nervously, but starting to feel happiness brewing in new little pinches in the bottom of her heart. On the outside she lies when Delois asks what kind of birthday cake she wants. She says chocolate, and she does want chocolate; but she wants Gabe more. The lie is, she won't be there.

Just before dawn the next day, she leaves three pictures, signed "Love ya,—Candy" for her brothers and sister and a note:

Mom and Dad,

Gabe and I are not scum, just in love.

To see me again, you have to love us the way I love you.

Candy

(P.S. I left you some songs. Sing'm in my new name, Billee.)

She slips out onto the street in her quietest shoes with her usual single bag of belongings to take to Gabe and makes her way down the gangster-ridden streets in near darkness, walking toward the park ahead. She can already see the line of the first light of day drawing a crossroads between yesterday and today. She's crying hard, deep inside, muffling everything, barely making a sound. Each step is heavy with the remorse of facing change she knows she is totally responsible for and almost alone with.

Gabe! There's the good old phone booth she used before that produces his image in her mind like an instant genie. She quickens her pace, lets down her bag, pulls open the squeaky glass door, and finds her coins. Then she dials.

"Gabe?" she chokes down the only word she can say, holding together a mixed spout of tears of desperation, confusion, hope, and love.

"Candy, I'm ready. Where are you?"

"In the park at the phone. Come get me. I'm 18 and scared for the sun to come up and show me here."

"Yes, but remember? It's okay now. It's okay. I'm coming right now."

"Please," She barely breathes out, softly, almost like last words.

She waits, not at all an eternity next to the murky booth at 43rd and Central, somehow frozen on the bench, stuffed with tears not to allow to explode. She's foot heavy, unable to stand or relax. She feels, as if before the world in testimony. Yes, like what others said before—like Patti Hearst when the cops burned down the Black Panthers shelter in 1974 in South Central and Patti was there. She stands the same as Patti, facing the world, but really merely talking to her parents and their world: "I cannot live like you. I have to have more."

Gabe pulls up behind, and in her tense shock she does not hear him. He sneaks up behind the bench and reaches warmly across her shoulders.

"Oh Gabe, it's you. Sit with me, a moment. I can't get up," she says softly.

He comes around and holds her close. When he sees her locked into a body of tears, he also breaks down, and the two hold each other in a massive release of long-stored pain, Gabe's face red with feeling and Candy's shiny wet. They don't talk but get into the car and leave.

When Gabe speaks, he says what Candy is thinking. "It's our emancipation. I know what to say. 'We're free, free at last!'"

CHAPTER FIVE

Free, Free at Last

The First Thirty Hours of the Next Thirty Years

Once the lovers are all cried out, they sleep (together) of pure exhaustion, shower (in the same shower stall), and wake to a whole new life—relaxed and full of sappy humor. Though nobody went to prison, it's as if both are getting out of prison. Everybody asks about their next plans, but Candy and Gabe just stare at them without an answer in the mushy mind-frame of honeymooners. Their point is the moment, even more than the future. They over-eat, under-eat, forget necessities and see no daily trials as mattering at all.

Gabe's birthday present is a new apartment. The old one is too expensive for someone who lost his teaching credential and job, and his mother's home is not a good fit. Their new home is a slightly cute, rundown, efficiency in crowded Korea Town, about halfway between South Central and Westwood. He drives her there directly from her hood park at sunrise, shows her the "Welcome, Candy" sign on their front door, unlocks it ceremoniously, and carries her in.

Candy laughs hard, as he sets her on her feet and onto the creaky floor. She says, "I never thought I'd see you carry me. I thought I was carrying you, that is, the whole team!" Then she adds, "Let's rest, clean our tear-sticky faces up and go out TOGETHER? I feel like being lavishly public."

So Gabe whisks them off to the famous Sunset Strip restaurant, The Source, a health food bistro where Candy gobbles up an organic beef burger as if she'd never seen one before and Gabe luxuriates in all you can do with exotic mixes of lettuce in an oversized, manly salad. They sit on the rue, watching gay men make the scene and the parading of America's most expensive cars spilling out of Beverly Hills. They schmooze around the strip like a pair of Mexicanos who just crossed the border for the first time. They giggle, kick trash, and periodically act like the high school types they once were,-- too loud, too silly, unpredictable, and generally unleashed.

East of the strip in the heart of Hollywood, after presiding over the stars' awards at Grauman's Chinese Theater, they slip down the block and into the Egyptian Theater with two tickets, both adult. They embed themselves in *Chariots of Fire*, film history's best-ever runner's story of hard won victory. The dark is perfect to sneak in kisses in what is likely the most beautiful cinema theater in the world, dripping in art deco gold design and wrapping them in deep purple velvet seats.

On the second day, Gabe goes off to work at the hardware store, and Candy takes the bus to Dorsey. She has two more months til graduation, and nothing, even Gabe, competes with that. Before they know it, the day is over, and they're preciously back together again. They finish whatever's left in the fridge, and it tastes like a Christmas meal. On weekends they're back at the Brentwood trail that in years to come will lead to the Getty Museum. All their haunts become famous over time, as do they.

The exterior of their apartment building is used later in the decade as the setting for Larry David's TV sitcom, Seinfeld, located at 757 South New Hampshire Avenue. It is a place for buffoons, and that's what they love to be together, Gabe resumes his corny jokes long lost in the classroom he left behind.

He says, "Baby, you're still cute, after all your suffering, the rough runs you won and the halting of all the runs you wanted and had to skip."

Standing 5'6" in nothing but her all-too-special running shirt from Jefferson, Candy is a beautiful sight to the man of her dreams, her body toned for action and her face shiny and glowing; her legs, their legs, outstandingly muscle taut, handsomely what their lives have always been about.

"YOU cute!" she tweaks back in South Centralese. They come together; they are together now. Candy's the first to get stuck in the Murphy bed. Laughing and yelling for help at the same time, Gabe saves her as usual and pulls her off the wall where she's wrapped up in the mattress that springs back when you least expect it.

"Not quite a honeymoon bed," she barks, "but I'm with a honey-man."

At this point many love stories fall apart over something important that has been thrown aside. But Candy and Gabe have already faced everything and love each other to the last breath like an old couple in their 80's. They already rest from a long trying history that never serves to do anything but bring them closer. A cup of chicken soup and a run in the glade peaks their day and sometimes is the gourmet dish that sets off the whole week. They do not fall apart; they dig in.

Once the talented relax, they breed energy and ideas, and this is what emerges immediately from Candy. No one will throw her off her emancipated course now, and certainly not Gabe. Together, they're stymied by the pro-White condition of the world, but there are few situations Candy does not find an answer for. No wonder, Gabe thinks, nothing stopped her in "pursuing my White ass."

Candy graduates in two short months from Dorsey with honors, but pertly accepts her certificate across an administration office counter, skipping the ceremony, beaming all the way home over her lapful of college scholarships. Gabe cannot spring back like Candy in the Murphy bed, though he does edge into some kind of school, a private middle school, Chatsworth Hills, where he has to teach math and regular subjects, a displaced coach edgy in the classroom.

A few weeks later, on just another happy Saturday morning, Candy rises to the sunshine like water evaporating, worshipping the beautiful LA weather of July 27, 1982.

She sings out like a poet: "We have to spend the day the way we used to, when you were my coach and I was your devoted slave runner!"

"What does that mean?" Gabe snorts, playing her game, equally swept up in the need to celebrate.

"We need to sprint around town, Griffith Park, the Hollywood Sign," she says, "and we could add in shops downtown, and oh, can't we go to The Pantry in the end? You know we're always starving in the end."

Gabe loves the same memories and places, especially the downtown 24/7 50's diner where people always go when too hungry and underpaid to consider feasting anywhere else. "You're on," he says, grabbing a light jacket for after sundown. "This is an all-day plan. Are you ready?"

"Um, hmm."

And they're off on what becomes an epic day in the history of the Grosz family. Does Candy steer Gabe into the jewelry district or do they fall upon it? Is she craving a wedding and a wedding ring, or does she simply fall in love with one she spies in a flashy window next to a pawn shop with an amazing display of Nike running shoes?

"Gabe, look at that."

"Look at what? Those shoes won't fit you."

"No, over here. That's a pretty ring. Isn't it?"

"Well, sure. It is. Do you want it? How much is it?"

"$125.00." She pauses, controlling the rest of her thoughts. "A lot, but it's—a—a wedding ring."

"Wow! A wedding ring. Do you want one, a wedding ring?"

Totally out of character, Candy says nothing and just looks at him, talking with her eyes. Gabe returns a wordless squinty-eyed stare, the two hug a long, sweet hug, and no more is said about the wedding ring. But outside, after the purchase and signing of a three-month payment plan, they start giggling together and assessing how many blocks to City Hall. City Hall clerks prove how easy it is to get a marriage license, providing a great rest stop on their all-day trek with a glamorous water fountain, bathrooms, and a lanai setting. Nothing is lost upon this fixated pair.

"What about the romantic part?" Candy asks, still giggly and surprised like Gabe. "I totally prefer The Pantry to a hotel wedding reception, but we need to do the 'I do' stuff, don't we?"

Before Gabe can reply, they both spot a Las Vegas style surprise, a wedding chapel sign on the joint across the street.

They ascend two flights of gritty stairs to the single dingy chapel room on floor two and sign more papers. It can be done today, now, in ten minutes, for $30.00!

The Justice of the Peace, Reverend Pallais, invites his wife to witness, and when he announces, "You are man and wife!" somehow all four have wet eyes, and Gabe kisses Candy with gusto, while the Reverend and his wife kiss too. What a kiss-a-thon! What a day! How celebrational! The two drown in giggles and an invisible glue that sticks them together, body to body, for the rest of the day.

"I guess," Candy records, "we're just fine marrying like this. This empty, scrubby place isn't really lonely or unspecial for us. I'm going to eat my heart out at The Pantry tonight, but first we have to touch base with our park and our Hollywood Sign."

In both spots they climb high at sunset to overlook the metropolis that had always thrilled them, and five hiking miles later, they anoint the Hollywood Sign with, not champagne, but bubbly Perrier.

"May the Force be with us!"

Candy laughs at their rituals, and they move back down and into the city they have conquered and now love together. Like the characters in Lucas' 1977 *Star Wars*, they live a life of intrigue, always as a wiry, wonderful team. By the time they reach The Pantry, it's at its best, past midnight and streaming with bright light in the heart of a downtown that is closing up. The diner's doing what it is there for, sparking night people's creativity with yummy, affordable food to eat in endless conversation.

Candy and Gabe have an early breakfast for their new life of eggs and sourdough bread, no champagne, no guests, and no gifts. They look and feel great together, prepared to take on a bigoted world. They look slightly unique when they squeeze up together, dark and warm-skinned Candy wearing a ring on her third finger, left hand, crunching up against thin, white and fair Gabe, flexing his leg muscles back on the sidewalk to half trot the long hike home.

A few weeks later, out of the blue, attorney Rubin calls.

"I have a surprise for you, Gabe. I went back to Judge Fitts to see if I could get him to dismiss your case from the records since you're now legally married, and he responded positively. We're in court again and bring your brainy wife. It'll be a pleasure to work with her for a change. We can prep in my office and head right on to court later in the morning, Saturday. That'll be the 13th, probably your lucky day."

The three bump heads perfectly Saturday, back at Rubin's Wilshire office, composing and signing statements about their relationship that validate a solid history of consensual love-making. Candy is totally in sync despite legal language and clarifications never offered her before. It is a memorable session, like a bunch of college activists prepping for a rally. All three finish with third-floor cafeteria French toast, part of Rubin's permanent dedication to fattening Gabe up. They march into court well-fed, well-trained, and giddy with expectation. Nonetheless, formality has it that the case is still called up as: "The people of the state of California vs. Gabriel Grosz."

Candy grimaces over the harsh-sound of the re-opening statement, but only in part. While she stares severely into the chamber, she periodically taps Gabe's hand in expectation, looking quizzically into his eyes for reassurance that this is almost fun. She's able to stand and state firmly and clearly that the two have been living together consensually since her eighteenth birthday and are now married, something she wishes her parents, team members, and friends were all there to hear announced. It's hard to stay seated calmly when the Rubin troupe finally hears the words "termination of probation" and "expungement of conviction."

Judge Fitts seems nearly as happy about Gabe's reinstatement himself, as he pronounces with a sense of embedded satisfaction: "I want to see you too without a criminal record, able to live your lives in the pursuit of happiness."

Meets You Can't Win and Meets You Can

With Candy by his side, Gabe at first feels each new challenge is like running another track race and winning. But there are things she cannot help him with. After the clearing of his record, he slumps instead of jumps, because there's still no coaching career. His applications are not going anywhere. He feels the interracial issue and "inappropriate coach conduct" are in the way. He needs new references without the old story in them.

Right after their hippy-style wedding day, Gabe receives another dead-end communication from the California Credential Board that leaves both flat-faced on the topic. Gabe, Mr. Reliability, succumbs this time to a bit of disappointment over the hopelessness of reestablishing himself. He says nothing, which is unlike him. When Candy asks what he'll do next, he acts like he doesn't care.

Later he moans out to Candy: "You're still able to do everything you wanted to in the first place. You just have to adjust to changing where you do it. The system's put me in no man's land. I just slump around in class. I want to coach!"

"Consider this," Candy says. "I know what we should

do, and I'll tell you later after a bowl of coleslaw and this steamed asparagus."

After dinner that night, Candy as always resets the apple cart. "This silly state does not love us," she pronounces. "I'm not going to UCLA or any of these California schools, scholarship or not. I'm going back to Union College in Schenectady. They want me and I want them, and you would like it too. We can stay with my grandma, and you can start over someplace where it's a whole different world for you. I'm homesick for New York." She sighs emotionally. "I'm just like Billie Holliday every time she felt finished with the LA scene. If I don't get us outa here, I'm gonna turn into a full-time permanent Blues singer."

"Schenectady's a pretty all-White town," Gabe counters.

"Always was, but it's not quite when I'm there. Even my Grandma Louise knows it's all about where you've been and what's already started to percolate in your heart. The last thing I want to do is keep following my crazy aunt Savanah around the country, looking for enclaves of Black talent. She's the one that picked South Central."

"Wait a minute, you 'racist' floosy, I picked South Central myself, and I was happy, and I found YOU there." Gabe plays the steady rock compared to Candy—the dreamer with so many ideas.

She smirks at him sweetly, planting a quick kiss on his neck. "We've got a Schenectady scholarship, a Schenectady grandma, and nostalgia. We've got love, love, and love. I don't hear Jefferson begging you to come back and wade through the grime 'n crime."

"YOU the 'man.' I can see where we're going," Gabe replies, the two ever speaking mock Centralese. After all, why not have a chicken in your pot while you're looking for the career job you want.

"I hope your Grandma Louise likes me better than your mom does," he says in full follower assent, and Candy starts to pack.

"I need her basement," she says. "I'm ready to sing some more jazz and my jazz's all basement or porch jazz. I can't do it in Korea Town! We need an awning and a glider or an old basement couch next to the furnace."

"We need more asparagus and coleslaw," says Gabe. "I'm in."

It's August 1982, and they're off to Schenectady, a poor decision at this point. Once there, things are bleaker than ever, with Gabe now forced with Grandma Louise's leadership to work as a hygienic aid for the disabled in a state facility for the aging, instead of running vibrant athletes around like gazelles. Candy tries several times by phone to resettle her past with her mom, but she fails also. She calls her, hoping to thrill her with their new residence in the same place Delois had herself long chosen to raise her daughter:

"Hi, Ma. It's me. How are you?"

"Since when do you care about how I am?"

"I've always cared, Ma."

"You have a funny way of show'n it, tak'n up with that White man."

"We're married, Ma. I have a ring and everything. Can't you at least wish us well?"

"Girl, I can't go anywhere that people don't look at me. Lord only knows what they must be thinking. But you don't care about that, do you?"

"I'm sorry. I love you, Ma, and Daddy too. Listen, I'm back in New York, going to go for my degree. I just want you to know everything is going to be okay."

"You still don't know anything. I don't like that White man. I can't see him ever being good to you."

Delois slams the phone down, and Candy thinks, *I have a lot of homework, but I'm gonna sing today.* And down in her grandma's basement she belts out better than ever, not a new song, but her oldest:

> Raindrops are falling so clear.
> I'm calling your name.
> It just ain't the same.
> Good times are a piece of the past.
> How could it last!
> Mama please hear my cry.

—Billee Mills, 1984

That night in bed, Candy tosses around and has a bad dream. She suddenly sits up and says, "I just saw my father's face in yours." She does not ever seem to remember this, but Gabe does. He remembers, but he never mentions it, knowing the demons she carries are unlikely to ever become clear to him, and that they are, after all, in the past. He is thankful for big wins, like being together, and small wins, like increasingly snuffing out more and more pains from their harsh start at Jefferson.

It's 1984 and they are not at their best at this time. But they know they are not their own problem, and that, even in the darkest rainstorm, they are the marathoners who always make it through. By this time there's everything at once: pregnancy, a sad job for Gabe, poor grades, scholastic probation, and no track team for Candy.

So, they load up the still-running car and reverse themselves West again. Chugging successfully back into what they now call The City of Angels, Candy dreams bigger than ever. She finds opportunity and checks it out with an incredible laser-like vision. She wastes little time, bringing her first child in utero to an obstetrician at the doorsteps of none other than trendy Brentwood, a sort of extension of Beverly Hills.

Gabe warns, "Brentwood's more than White. It's pristine. It's White-thinking. What are we doing here?" But he can't believe how suddenly she leaps into the unknown. He also knows how hard she works and how often she achieves exactly what she wants. Next, she wants a Brentwood apartment. He says, "We can look at the place in this ad, but I see no way they'll accept us or our budget."

But Candy's eye senses the perfect place, a beautiful 1940's style building, and open house snooping pulls her to the trendy apartment like a magnet. It sits on the north side of Sunset Boulevard. Gabe decides to play no role at all in this. He feels it's nothing but wishful thinking.

It's amazing how trained Gabe and Candy are to handle change. They get out of their small worn car and approach the Parisian feng shui entrance gate as if accustomed to the ambiance. They love it and find the price amazingly accommodating. The manager smiles warmly at the very interracial couple and child.

"It's yours if you want it," she says.

"Are you sure our application meets your standards?" Gabe feels compelled to add.

He remembers how hard it was to beat out competitors for the run-down efficiency in Korea Town.

"I'm sure," she offers. "Do you want to know a secret about this place?"

"Yes," Candy and Gabe say, hunching up together, expecting to hear that it's haunted or the scene of a recent murder.

"You've won something like a diversity lottery," she says with a huge smile. "I'm picking you two out of 43 others because you're the only charming, cute interracial couple who has applied. I've been waiting for someone like you to show up for three months. Since the 60's, I've been an activist for civil rights and I want to be sure I can give it to somebody who needs a break. I'm picking you.

At this astounding moment, the Groszes, all two and a half of them, settle easily into a lovely lifestyle that instantly erases the sting of their ill-fated struggles in Schenectady and recharges the inborn optimism that brought them together in the first place.

They wonder if the school board is similarly encouraged by the right address, as Candy immediately applies for Gabe with the new address to the California Credentials Board for Gabe's reinstatement as a teacher, and magic takes place. In a short week, his teaching credential is reinstated and takes with that a much-appreciated LA Job Corp position. It's not coaching, but for Gabe, a huge move out of the classroom and into a training mode.

Surprisingly, the home-again mood even reaches Delois, who offers the two some time in her home before they move into their new apartment. Tony and Jeaneen are both home and dying to see their sister, interestingly fat with Gabriela inside.

They want her to tell New York stories on the porch, race them to the end of the block, then straight 'round the Jefferson track again, and up and down the porch stairs at home, until Candy finally sinks into her favorite rickety porch glider with labored breath.

She says, "Okay, you two win on these races, Jefferson track, cross country there and back, and stairs for hurdling. You're only catching up with me because I'm pregnant. We're going to do this again after Gabriela's born. She and I will both beat you two, three years from now. That's our contract . . . unless I train her and not you two?"

Tony and Jeaneen love this.

"Okay. Let's go back to school. R-e-a-d-y . . .N ow!"

They beg to start one more race.

"No, we're not," says Candy. "You don't know anything about late pregnancy. Bring me a little blanket and some lemonade and submit your training requests next year after we see if Baby Gabriela looks like a runner. I'm not going to train everybody in this family. Let me stretch out here now and just sing. This porch has always been my best singing spot."

Who can believe how Gabe is received, the surprise victory for the Groszes bringing Delois' Black princess home pregnant, plump and tired, but happier than ever because of him, the man Delois tried to destroy—legally, emotionally, even with physical violence. As she first opens the door to her daughter, arm in arm with her alleged sexual attacker, Delois' words ring out like the proclamation of the century, "What the hell. You're my son-in-law now. Earl, get in here and get a look at these two. . . 'n lock those old guns up tight, all of''m."

Surprisingly, very surprisingly, Delois crosses the threshold and embraces Gabe. He stands a bit stiff but is a good receiver. Speechless with shock, it's his eyes that hold her tight. He has a bag of avocados in his hand, and he thrusts it into hers.

"Guacamole!" she says and runs off to the kitchen to stay safe on her queen-mom turf.

But Gabe, master of friendship, follows her, peeking his head around the corner into the kitchen. "Really, guacamole?" he echoes.

"Green as a Jew in South Central," she says.

"I didn't know you are a clever woman. Now, I understand why my wife is so smart," Gabe smirks, good with just about anybody.

"Cleverer than you," Delois says. "This here's a woman's house mostly. If you remember that and take out the garbage, you'll shine around here, at least a little bit."

Gabe frankly loves guacamole, which luckily remains his major memory of their first two weeks back home.

A Wing and a Prayer

The first of the next 30 years flies by on a wing and a prayer. Gabe stays employed for some time by the seat of his pants, and later in a variety of basic positions. None of the first matches the glory and fascination of coaching track with Candy on his team in South Central. But she operates in surges of creative energy, always starting with the same sweet twist of her smile as she puts the same thought to Gabe again and again over time:

"Baby, I have an idea. I've always wanted to . . ."

She regularly turns him into a willing accomplice, achieving one dream after another, possibly exalting her to the most indulged wife ever. From 1982 to 2002, every yes between Candy and Gabe leads to a phenomenal product. Racial insults plump Candy's pout almost like fertilizer, while Gabe's calm charisma surrounds and protects her in an aura of gentility.

A magnificent start is the beautiful Gabriela's birth in 1984 at UCLA Medical Center near Beverly Hills. It shocks the entire hospital. Gabe faces the payment clerk meekly, to hear her say, "Your Obstetric bill, Mr. Grosz, is $10,000. How do you intend to pay it? "We just don't have $10,000," he responds. "All I can pay is $10.00 a month."

He tries to keep money matters out of Candy's way and waits patiently through endless paperwork to prove their poverty on hospital payment forms. After much whispering among personnel and stares from each of them, the very kind clerk takes his hand and melts the stress of the situation. She looks warmly into his eyes.

"Mr. Grosz, as of this very moment, despite its uniqueness for our office, you do have a welfare excuse for payment, and I want you to know I look forward to seeing Candy and Gabriela myself. She'll be my first Black baby at UCLA, and I want you to know your family is so welcome here."

Upstairs Candy is grabbing for her clothes, eager to leave the hospital two days early. She wreaks a similar surprise for the hospital on her floor. "Gabe, Baby, I don't need three days here. I only need one day here with Gabriela." She offers to the nurse, "We're ready to leave now. Can you bring my baby, please?"

"Oh no. There must be some mistake, Ma'am. We did not have any Black babies born this week at UCLA."

"I'll take, in that case, the best you've got, that beautiful White-looking one named Gabriela. She happens to be mine, fresh out of the womb!"

Candy looks and sounds severe, but as ever, she carries the painful effort and satisfaction of a winner. Gabriela is the Whitest and incidentally the most beautiful baby on the floor. Consequently, Candy, blushing deep berry Black, leaves the hospital with a free White-as-porcelain baby (very hers) and a welfare-paid receipt, both surprise exceptions to hospital records. Best of all is Candy's inner resolution, as if she'd intended Gabriela to be as White as she could be. She faces all challenges remembering that, on the track, she outruns everyone. So when she thinks she might be a little right, she feels instead, a lot right.

In the spirit of the balance of fate, eight years later at the same hospital Candy gives birth to son, Lazlo, with no drama at all. He is also a "free" baby, born in the same posh hospital, another perfect racial fit to his dad, calmly suiting the attitudes of the world.

It is as though the personality game of the genes is to match Candy to Gabriela—in mystique, creativity, and outreach, and Gabe to Laszlo—in stoic and quiet confidence. This is the history of a family that moves forward, becomes famous for their story, and will shortly be asked to project their image in TIME magazine.

Stop Stopping Candy

Candy is always compelled by the taste of success, and the bite of ideas sits stirring on the window sill. She and Gabe live with that mood and never have quite enough bad luck to forget their Jefferson teamwork.

"Gabe, Baby, I always meant to get my degree at Union and set track records. I always expected you to coach again." She throws her agile body at him, knocking him onto the bed, planting kisses onto his face and adding, "I want you to coach me again. I meant all this stuff for us, but I just couldn't calm down enough to do it the last time we were at Union."

As always, Gabe at first looks at her silently and wide-eyed. Then, knowing there's no stopping Candy and that her failures in Schenectady are atypical for her, he merely listens, wondering—*Dear God, where are we going next?*

"I know," he says. "There's something right about cleaning up our messes. When the Dean suspended you, he said you can return after probation, but he didn't think you would ever graduate from Union. I remember what you said back to him. You said, 'Oh, I will. You just watch. You just wait and see.' Candy, he doesn't know you. I get it. You can count on me. I'm in. Let's do it. Let's go back to Schenectady and fix everything we foiled."

We all know we "cannot go back," but never say never to Candy (or Gabe). Four years later they both achieve surprises while at Union College, starting with a New York State teaching credential for Gabe and two jobs--coaching Cross Country and Track at Candy's former high school, assistant track coaching at Union, and finally Candy graduating with honors in Economics and a slate of new records for her, unbroken to this day in the long jump, 60-meter dash, and 300-meter run. They finally achieve a return to their dream to be coach and runner together again, to win as ever, and to reignite Candy's lifetime dream of Olympic training.

Gabe says, "Baby, you did it, everything, but you're a little young to retire." They're four years into Schenectady life. He's puckering up a sweet kiss for Gabriela on her first birthday and a super embrace for the amazing woman of his dreams. "What's next, the Olympics?"

"It has to be, Gabe, down the line, but take another picture of me holding up Gabriela to blow out her candle. Do you know I've got these filed? Don't laugh. I file'm under races and race-combos. See, this shot goes under race combos. Gabriela and I as kid and mom are a race-combo shot."

"Who cares? I don't get it."

At this, Candy takes him to the back hallway floor, smothered in hundreds of pictures lined up based on varieties of racial mix. He says, "Are you going to grad school in sociology or what?"

"No. I'm celebrating. I'm going into my celebration phase, not just for us but for everybody like us. All these people I found around here, around the neighborhood. They start asking me about how Gabriela is my daughter, and then they start telling their stories and giving me pictures. Probably no humans anywhere are one hundred percent racially pure. And who needs it?"

In a very few minutes, Candy entices Gabe into her plan. They spend the next two hours on the hall floor drinking tea, Gabriela bouncing from lap to lap, as they study the photos. Candy says, "I'm going to start the world's first interracial magazine and astound hardheads like some I could name at Jefferson. It's going to soothe our hurt and the hurt of a lot of other people. I already have a list of first subscribers. Famous or not, I think we may make some money for a change."

Gabe long ago stopped stopping Candy and merely asks her not to publish his worst shots, which would be most of his pictures at that point. His concern is spot on. In November 1989, he and Candy emerge smiling together on the cover of the first issue of their very own *Interrace* magazine. In a matter of months, the media not only includes *Interrace*, with a circulation of 25,000, but the entire exciting Grosz' story. Candy is proven wrong in her predictions of little fame and money. *Interrace* brings in a lot of both.

They launch their project with Gabe's mere $1,000 that leads to a $75,000 corporate buyout offer with a chief editor position and New York City apartment, and their humble turndown has no effect on their fame. CNN picks up their story from local Schenectady news, immediately followed by *NPR, AP, UPI, Good Morning Boston* and *Philadelphia*, Ronald Reagan's son's TV talk show, and *USA Today*. Instead, she happily continues to develop more interracial journalism on her own: *Biracial Child* magazine, *Black Child* (for parenting), interracial greeting cards, and a first interracial coloring book for kids, *Mommy, Mommy—What Color Am I?*

Major newspapers and magazines exaggerate the blitz, from *The Los Angeles Times, New York Times,* and *Washington Post* to non-stop TV talk shows, including: *Geraldo, Sally Jesse Raphael, Ricki Lake, Jenny Jones,* and *Donahue* twice, once with interracial couples and later featuring the Groszes (as teacher/student). Letting their hair down instead of tiptoeing painfully around the force of their attraction feels like Mardi Gras style release.

"What happens at Las Vegas STAYS at Las Vegas," no matter how many millions view it. Once introduced as an icon, the world sometimes invites the outspoken to speak. The release proves a thrill for Candy and Gabe that brings out their genuine selves and true responses to all those entrapment questions one can spend a lifetime avoiding. The following WBBM-TV Chicago, 1992 Transcript fully bounces off the TV screen from the Donahue Show.

Phil Donahue Show in Progress
Candy and Gabe are the featured guests.

<u>Donahue:</u> Okay, audience. You're so smart . . . Who's he and who's she? Huh?

Audience member: He's her track coach!

Donahue: How'd you know that?

Audience member: It was on *CNN Headline News.*

Donahue: Well, that means it's fact. Gabe really was Candy's track coach. Incidentally, Candy in 1981 ran the second-fastest time in the country in the low hurdles.

(Audience applauds.)

Donahue: Candy, you were 16 when you began dating the coach.

Candy: Dating . . . no.

Donahue: Uh . . .

Candy: It wasn't like that. He wasn't my boyfriend. Mr. Grosz was my coach.

Donahue: Your coach, huh? I see . . .

Candy: I was calling him Mr. Grosz two years after I married him.

(Audience giggles.)

Donahue: Hang on! Hold it! I'm starting to get a headache. We want to give you time to tell this story. We should make it a point that you've been married now for nine years.

(Audience applauds.)

Candy: Going on ten.

Donahue: Candy, your parents didn't like this even a little bit.

Candy: No.

Donahue: They made their statement by what?

Candy: Taking him to court.

Donohue: Candy, you testified against Gabe.

Candy: Yes.

(The audience listens intently, glued to every word.)

Donahue: At the trial, in your opinion, what was the most damaging thing you said against what was then your future husband?

Candy: That I didn't love him.

Donahue: And you knew that wasn't true?

(Candy takes a moment to ponder her answer.)

Candy: I liked him. I mean, I loved Gabe, but he was my teacher. He was my coach. I didn't like that part of it.

Donahue: In fact, you were calling him Mr. Grosz after you had sex.

Candy: I was calling him Mr. Grosz during.

(The audience bursts into wild and euphoric laughter and clapping, and Donahue holds up a copy of *Interrace* magazine!)

Donahue: Gabe? What do you have to say? The legal burden was on you.

Gabe: Legal Beagle—I'm a man of my word, and the words were "I love you." Our story is all about love. The rest is someone else's problem.

Picking Promotion

Not much could top so much spotlight on the issue the Groszes hold dear, but Gabe especially treasures the interracial couple article that followed the same year in TIME.

Candy, Gabe, Gabriela, and Laszlo are pictured together, Sunday church style, in all their natural glory. TIME, he says, is a mark of public acceptance. It's like a pat on the back from the speaker of your clan.

Gabe and Candy connect, not oddly, but perfectly as lovers. Their story is more important than the horrid nervous error of Romeo and Juliet and the vicious desperation of Bonnie and Clyde. It has rather the character of a classic Greek tale. Gabe in manly fashion is willing to take on full public punishment for their "crime," and Candy with womanly warmth offers complex healing explanation. Heroically, they never question themselves and risk everything for each other.

It all seems like the lemmings last dance! Why is there never time to reset Olympic training plans? Both of them know age is a dangerous issue for Candy 's athletics that can take control before she knows it. "As soon as I get out my CD's," she assures Gabe and her singer-songwriter self, the Olympics will be next.

But these two are in their magical phase, and in 1998, when Candy finally belts out her musical teenage memories at a cool and famous recording studio in Hollywood, she's a Black Janis Joplin breaking the sound barrier. It takes them beyond success. She closes her last song, (the first composed) "If You Could See Me Now," in a mean slap of voice and follows off-tape, yelling, "Whoa, Baby!" at Gabe, as she falls into a cushy West Hollywood leather couch, her eyes aglow, rolling around and staring at the ceiling as if it were heaven. "While I still have breath left, let God give us a way to give back!"

Gabe says, "These three songs are enough. You gave at the office, Candy."

He takes out a handkerchief, mops up her brow, and softly pushes her bangs off her forehead.

"You got it. This is a great start to your album. Where's the champagne? It's 1998. We should save a bottle of Dom Perignon 1998. Oh, stop me! We don't drink."

She removes her headset, but instead of joining him, slumps suddenly, a furrow in her beautiful sweaty brow. She stops. Something is wrong. She winces and looks at her left leg.

"What is it?"

"Something, a twitch in my leg." In jest she adds, "With my luck it's probably MS."

"Come on, don't talk like that. If it doesn't go away by tomorrow, we'll go see what the doctor has to say."

"Oh, forget my twitches," she says, still drunk on the obvious success of her bluesy album. "I want champagne for all of us, Beverly Hills, sequined gowns, celebrity and awards."

Candy seems to be looking at a vision.

As usual when she explodes into an idea, Gabe's eyes swell while he waits in silence to find out what's going on. He pulls her up. "Okay now, sit up and talk straight."

So she does, not enough to lapse back into earlier plans for Olympic training, but within a few short months, her vision of glitter, champagne, of a grand award ceremony at the Beverly Hills Hotel works its way into a fabulous reality. Candy sets up a plan, not to award just athletes, singers, or scholars. She creates and delivers the first-ever award ceremony for interracial activists, leaving her salty songs moaning on the porch and in her New York grandma's basement where she wrote them. She calls her new Los Angeles event "The Loving Awards."

The event is paid for by $50.00 tickets for attendees who Candy simply advertises to cold in the newspaper. The famous Dizzy Gillespie, Jazz Bebop Icon, sparks the affair encouraging interracial musicians, while others like Dan O'Brien, 1992 Olympic Gold Medal Decathlon Winner celebrates athletes. Dizzy is Candy's touch of warmth, fresh off the cover of one of her *Interrace* magazines. She awards "Best Children's Book for Biracial Children," "Best Biracial Athlete," and others who discovered and promoted biracial success.

Candy wears the dress she never wore to a prom with her favorite prom-less date also in formal attire. A Disney-style sky of sparkling stars crowns the night, and life seems and is perfect. Gabriela and Laszlo attend to drink bubbly juice and tap dance in the halls.

On the edge of all this promotion are the doctors. A short time later, they confirm the MS she fears, though Candy continues characteristically to ignore her painful twitches. She does not stop her regular runs with Gabe in Brentwood and Griffith Park. But soon after the awards event, in running gear, on the same road up to the Hollywood Sign they'd always run with the Jefferson team, the struggles becomes too hard, and she has to stop. She looks up toward the summit and doubles her fist at the sky." FUCK YOU, MS!"

This was the first and only time Gabe ever heard her use the "F" word. It meant pain, and he feared to think of hearing it again.

CHAPTER SIX

On Last Legs Together

This is the year of not only so much success, but also the crash. Too soon, it is the end of their stolen love story influencing the universe on foot, in song, and in celebration—GONE! On their next regular Brentwood Hills run, all this grand aspiration decompresses instantly and cruelly. Candy's soul, and of course Gabe's, are burst like pricked balloons. Candy's pain stops them on the trail and the doctors insist on extreme restraint, a strike against her life force whose instincts rule. She is quickly thrown into a slow debilitation toward inevitable death.

This has to be talked through, faced. Can their chance to make their own story be stolen from them again, this time without violence, cops, Delois unglued, and joblessness? The Groszes had made peace in their hearts with everyone, and Candy had advanced to the position of fairy godmother to the interracial world. She had finally begun to deal with the former wish to belt out her songs and restart Olympic training.

As if in one minute every dream can come true, in another, every dream can be mysteriously and suddenly snuffed out. It's many years later, during her painfully long and slow decline, that Gabe saves her extra footsteps to cross the bedroom. He brings her something special from the bureau for her to open, an interesting-looking letter from the California Correctional Facility in Tehachapi. It has a big gray and green stamp on it honoring California field workers and opens to water-marked manilla stationery. It says essentially:

Dear Mrs. Mills,
Our facility has long admired your work to stabilize the lives of the many victims of unjustified prejudice. Your athletic record, personal legal stamina, interracial journalism, public voice, and singer-songwriter solos have won the hearts of many of our inmates.

We sincerely hope that you will be able to schedule a vocal performance for 700 of our qualified inmates sometime this year.

We'd like to share with you the appreciation we shared with Johnny Cash for the healing power of music from the soul. We hope you can help us move forward with the music tradition at our facility that Johnny started.

The letter brings tears of awe for Candy. It's an achievement just to have been asked. But answering, "No. I am so sorry, but I am now chronically ill," is too painful. This is another, the last of her lifelong dreams, to have to bypass. It is painfully clear she was born with enough spirit for all her copious wishes, but a blunting turn of fate has now halted everything.

Gabe spares her the letter of decline, writing it for her, and mailing it off quickly. He then keeps the invitation letter on the bureau where she can see it all the time.

Oh, lady of vim and vigor, remember who you are inside!

She does and he does and time crawls forth now on what some close couples call "four legs" or "four eyes." Candy and Gabe have a common inner voice now that speaks the same inside. It pretty much says, "What the hell?" and stops there, knowing no other way to put it.

"Well, Babe," Gabe says, "I guess we should've made more time for prayer or meditation in our lives, or something."

"No, Baby," she says, stretched out on the couch, rubbing her once miraculous legs. "Thoreau's always been enough for me. I'll take'm to the hospital or wherever. But did you hear about his weak side? He was a kind of a fake who talked about living in inspiring simplicity alone, when in reality, he took his laundry to his mom every two weeks through the whole famous "isolation" experiment. This genius couldn't even handle an armload of dirty clothes! I guess I won't be a mountain of inspiration to anybody anymore, but I still love Henry David T. and YOU."

"It's all for love. That's all I ever said. We've got that. You've got that, and it's pretty hard to see a whole lot coming from anything else. You just skip athletics, music, projects, money, fame—and sit around feeling loved. You'll still be ahead of the whole human race if that's all you do."

Candy and Gabe are glued upon each other and drift far away from the cold cruel world easily at this point. They make love after this discussion. Her body still seems smooth and warm and well, and so does his. After nearly 30 years now, eating right, running and frankly carving their bodies into one beautiful image, they fold into each other warmly and softly with a rhapsody even greater than their first, because. . . because they know this time might be the last!

Things Change

An altered universe both quickly and gradually sets in, a hospital existence, life about Candy but not really with Candy, caregiving from all, from Gabe till he is 62, losing hair and wearing glasses, and from Laszlo until he is 22 and Gabriela 30.They eat so many meals in their mom's room that they scatter it with fast food wrappers and drink cups until they decide to distract her eye by wall-papering the whole space in posters that can make her smile inside: *Breakfast at Tiffany's*, Frank Sinatra, Jim Ryun, and Jimi Hendrix. They play CD's for her and read to her, especially a little Thoreau every day.

Time creeps painfully on, as the little troupe drudgingly hands out meds, linens, massages, stale jokes and hopeless encouragement. Gabe massages her thin, thin legs that not only have stopped running, but stopped all things legs are for. Without her verve, ideas, and vision for her sweet, progressive horde, Candy's family is deflated, all searching for the specialness they used to have, one by one discovering she has always been their major drive. Increasingly, Gabe knows their epic tale is sinking with Candy's deterioration and the remaining family is now more average people with less exciting hopes and actions, care givers like others everywhere, locked into the joy of support, sometimes with little energy or heart for more.

One unusually tedious day, --after years bedridden, with little movement and very few words, Candy suddenly senses that she is about to die. She seems to slip further from everyone. Before she can't communicate any more, she wants to square away things with Gabe. She gestures for him to sit beside her on her bed, a spot where she has memorized every wrinkle of the sheet, every line in the patterns in the bedspread, and where assisted to take one more sip of water or not becomes the insanely boring next decision. Should she sip more before noon or after? Who cares? Still, Gabe and the kids will each come in and ask her, "Do you want help taking another sip?"

On this day, she calls Gabe over and talks to him. For her, Gabe looks as though he is standing so high. It's as if he is above her on the ceiling looking down. She does not brave the pain of sitting up. She begs him to listen carefully and closely as she whispers what prove her final shared thoughts. "I'm thinking." Here she stops. "At least I'm thinking," she says. "That's all I do . . . think!" She takes a break here between thoughts that take too much energy to get out. "What about our . . . fabulous felony?"

"What do you mean? Are you in a twilight state? Do you want another sip of water?"

"No. Sometimes lemonade; it all tastes the same. I'm finished sipping. Promise me you'll never mention sips again? I'm thinking everything's come down to 'how-many-sips-a-day?'"

At this, Gabe smooths out the linens around her and sweetly and delicately refolds the place where they come to rest on her chest.

"Will you remember everything we did . . .?" she asks as if genuinely worried that something will be forgotten. Here she coughs and takes another break. "Our—fabulous felony?"

"Oh no, Baby. I forgot the felony a long time ago. I'm sorry about all that. That was my felony, not yours."

"Oh, God, this is cute, an argument, a final chance to have a real-but-smiling argument, and I'm dying! You say it was your felony, but I seduced you." Here she breaks again, swallows hard, and continues. "We were either both aggressors or both victims. You'd better give this 'victim' another kiss right now. I want to be sure it's still worth it."

Gabe reaches down from what looks to her to be the ceiling and kisses her slowly three times, with a pause between each and a lovely stare into her eyes.

"So, Candy, you want to share the felony? Do you want me to call the lawyer, call Rubin and tell him you want your half of the guilt . . . before you die?"

"Yeah. good. I always liked working with you. I like the way you handle things." At this she laughs a little, though it hurts to do so, but she does laugh. This is probably her last laugh, and her words come out much more slowly than she thinks them. She has to stop long between phrases, no matter how peppy the message.

"I'm thinking what a fabulous felony it was," she sighs. "That's why I want to die—a co-conspirator."

She tries to sit up to say the last part, so Gabe helps her and holds her up so they are almost face to face.

She says, "Help me with this final section. I want to try to finish—not sure I can talk more."

Gabe grimaces, but looks her squarely and seriously in the face to hear her pronounce her own bizarre legal summary:

"Do you, Gabriel Grosz, take this felony until death do we part, in sickness and in health, in shame and loss, in fines, lawyer bills, jail threats and ignominy (I practiced that word while you were downstairs.), in pure desire, lust, trust, and romance with Candy Mills until she is willing to breathe her last breath?"

At this, she painfully acts out a two-handed self-strangulation, smiling pathetically and looking at him for his reaction to the punch line.

Gabe smirks dumbly, lost in giddy love. "Yes. Of course. I accept you as totally contagious, conceited, gorgeous, and complicit." He holds her up in a deep embrace, wishing Gabriela were there to videotape her mom's last cogent conversation, or that it was a scene in a movie everyone would see, or a book everyone would read. He'd never been and never would be embarrassed for matching up with Candy, and Gabriela and Laszlo had also been comfortable with their famous parents' struggle to be together, and even a little proud of their publicity and peppy rants.

The kids found, over the years, their young friends not interested in adult free-love issues. So, the profane points of discussion that mark even their mom's last days seem normal and nearly race past them. It all brings tears to Gabe's eyes and leaves the kids sober and polite, as they have learned to be in such a passionate and overheard family. The two tip-toe around the scene, used to their mom being almost comatose, and not speaking like this. They do not realize she is high on her last wind. They break into the end of her excruciating attempt to speak for the first time in months.

"Mom, you're stronger today, at least this minute," Gabriela sings out like a breath of fresh air. She cuts the deadness of the room with her energy and finds a spark of life she has not long seen in her mom's eyes. This makes her look at her father in wonder until she sees him nod, and she knows he knows this is a beautiful surprise, a special last moment.

"Here's a pink flower, Mom. They have'm downstairs," Laszlo adds, not knowing what else to say and feeling nervous to see something precious is happening with his mom that may not ever happen again.

"Kids?" Gabe calls in a whisper, grabbing them both around the middle. "Your mom is straining her voice, but I think she has more she wants to say. Let's not chat, just listen. You can snuggle up quietly with her in the bed. I'll tuck you all in together." He's satisfied at the thought of them all of them in Candy's bed together, a feat, but a grand one for an athletic family.

Candy struggles to get more comfortable, and Gabe helps her adjust her position, one kid tucking her in like a giant pillow on each side. She pushes out a complaint in a fallen voice, "I wish I could sing . . . right now."

"Candy, few people ever really sing, but you did, and don't forget it's all on tape. Do you want me to play one of your CD's?"

"No . . . Do Thoreau, page 42. . . and again, after I'm gone."

"Okay," says Gabe, as he brings her stained and ragged favorite book to her side and reads Thoreau's comment, marked by her in red ink with a tiny red heart drawn next to it: "There is no remedy for love but to love more."

"It goes with our fabulous felony," she says. She looks at him deeply and slowly. "Put that on my urn, okay? 'Candy and Gabe committed a fabulous felony, but it is only that they could do no other; for there is no remedy for love but to love more.'"

"Yes," he answers, whispering and deeply touched. He shushes the kids and gestures them out of bed and holds Candy closely, faint and distant now, until she falls asleep. At this, the kids slink quietly out and leave their parents respectfully alone.

Following this bedroom event, Candy says nothing, really nothing. She says nothing for months, bogged down by the sinking struggle of death, and quieted by the satisfaction of having already said and done it all.

Months later, on November 25, 2014, she speaks out from beneath a long quiet period just one more word, only one this time. . . "Gabe?" and drops down into the soft sheets that encase her warmly as Gabe always set them.

She is no longer alive, just another thing that Mother Nature has stopped and lain aside. She is emancipated now, really free, as free as she can get, as free as love can get you.

EPITAPH

We're not yet so spoken and spent, but she is, and she who opened doors deserves fresh air. For Gabe, Candy haunts Hollywood, the place full of ghosts, so he climbs the hill to the Hollywood Sign she loved and sets her ashes into the breeze there that she always craved.

We record Candy's early death and the end of her illness, her blues songs slated to be sung to 700 prison-mates at Tehachapi, an ash trail left at the HOLLYWOOD sign, a record athlete's persistence that froze competitors and shored-up peers, and an intelligence that defined and opened new ways of life. She ran an Olympic-style torch where others merely dozed.

Gabe was her man and eventually the favorite of her mom's relatives. He received one first and last call from Candy's father on the very day she died. Earl said, "Man, I have to tell you. You're the one who stayed with ma'daughter through thick 'n thin. Thanks."

Gabe now wins senior races more than 40 years later and remains close today to the other characters in this tale. Though Candy lost her athletic abilities through a trick of fate, some of Gabe's former male South Central runners are hardy track coaches today. They continue to follow Gabe's "live it and love it," twenty-four-seven training style. The children of Candy and Gabe, Gabriela and Laszlo, assert their biracial selves in a current, slightly more compassionate world, remembering the young Black mom they loved and sharing life with the older White dad they still have. Gabe lives near them in Boulder, Colorado.

Excerpt from *The Souls of Black Folk* by W.E.B. Du Bois 1903

Between me and the other world there is ever an unasked question; unasked by some through feelings of delicacy, by others through the difficulty of rightly framing it. All, nevertheless, flutter round it. They approach me in a half-hesitant sort of way, eye me curiously or compassionately, and then, instead of saying directly, "How does it feel to be a problem? they say, "I know an excellent colored man in my town, or I fought at Mechanicsville, or do not these Southern outrages make your blood boil?

At these I smile or am interested, or reduce the boiling to a simmer, as the occasion may require. To the real question, how does it feel to be a problem? I answer seldom a word.

About the Author

Chris Cryer, Instructor of Critical Thinking and Literature at Ventura College, comes from the deep South, where she was aligned with interracial issues in administration at Tuskegee U. in Alabama, in Head Start in Florida, and in a public Montessori Title I program in Tennessee, all predominately Black populations where she met hard-working Black women like Candy, also busy opening hearts and minds.

She has written two books, a textbook, *Basic College Essay Guide*, that served years of college students, and her memoir, *Tolstoy in Riyadh*, which won the Paris Festival Award for Best Biography, the North Texas Book Award for Non-fiction, and was nominated for the Pushcart Prize. Chris' film and book reviews were regular for *The LA Times County Edition* and the *LA Levantine Cultural Center Newsletter* through 2015.

Dedicated to expanding the voices of the least understood, Cryer's textbook rages against distaste for commas, and her Saudi book unveils the little-known gentility of Saudi men. In *A True Love Story from South Central*, she takes up the voice of now-deceased Candy Grosz to continue to press for relationship rights for those who need to put culture last and love first.

CPSIA information can be obtained
at www.ICGtesting.com
Printed in the USA
FSHW020707241121